D1065830

*Merrill*

# Advanced Mathematical Concepts

*Precalculus with Applications*

# PRACTICE MASTERS

## GLENCOE

McGraw-Hill

New York, New York
Columbus, Ohio
Mission Hills, California
Peoria, Illinois

Copyright © by Glencoe/McGraw-Hill.

All rights reserved. Permission is granted to reproduce the material contained herein on the condition that such material be reproduced only for classroom use; be provided to students, teachers, and families without charge; and be used solely in conjunction with *Merrill Advanced Mathematical Concepts*. Any other reproduction, for use or sale, is prohibited without prior written permission of the publisher.

Send all inquiries to:
Glencoe/McGraw-Hill
936 Eastwind Drive
Westerville, OH 43081

ISBN: 0-02-824292-0

Printed in the United States of America.

5 6 7 8 9 10 11 12 13 14 15    009    03 02 01 00 99 98 97

# CONTENTS

Glencoe Division, Macmillan/McGraw-Hill

# CONTENTS

Glencoe Division, Macmillan/McGraw-Hill

## 1-1 Practice Worksheet

## Relations and Functions

**State the domain and range of each relation. Then state whether the relation is a function. Write yes or no.**

**1.** $\{(-1, 2), (3, 10), (-2, 20), (3, 11)\}$

**2.** $\{(0, 2), (13, 6), (2, 2), (3, 1)\}$

**3.** $\{(1, 4), (2, 8), (3, 24)\}$

**4.** $\{(-1, -2), (3, 54), (-2, -16), (3, 81)\}$

**Given that x is an integer, state the relation representing each of the following by listing a set of ordered pairs. Then state whether the relation is a function. Write yes or no.**

**5.** $y = 3x^2 - 5$ and $0 < x < 5$

**6.** $y^2 = 3x^2$ and $x = -3$

**7.** $|3y + 4| = x$ and $0 < x < 3$

**8.** $|y| = |x|$ and $0 < x < 2$

**The symbol [x] means the greatest integer not greater than x. If f(x) = [2x] – 3x, find each value.**

**9.** $f(0)$

**10.** $f(0.5)$

**11.** $f(-3.5)$

**12.** $f(x - 1)$

**Given f(x) = |3x – 4| + 5, find each value.**

**13.** $f\left(\dfrac{1}{3}\right)$

**14.** $f(0.5)$

**15.** $f(-0.5)$

**16.** $f(5d)$

**Name all values of x that are not in the domain of the given function.**

**17.** $f(x) = \dfrac{x - 2}{x + 4}$

**18.** $f(x) = \dfrac{1}{|2x + 5|}$

**19.** $f(x) = \sqrt{x^2 - 25}$

**20.** $f(x) = \dfrac{x - 10}{\sqrt{x^2 - 16}}$

**21.** $f(x) = \dfrac{x^2 + 25}{x^2 - 25}$

**22.** $f(x) = \dfrac{x - 7}{x^2 - 1}$

Glencoe Division, Macmillan/McGraw-Hill

# 1-1 Practice Worksheet

## Relations and Functions

*State the domain and range of each relation. Then state whether the relation is a function. Write yes or no.*

**1.** $\{(-1, 2), (3, 10), (-2, 20), (3, 11)\}$
$\{-2, -1, 3\}, \{2, 10, 11, 20\}$; no

**2.** $\{(0, 2), (13, 6), (2, 2), (3, 1)$
$\{0, 2, 3, 13\}, \{1, 2, 6\}$; yes

**3.** $\{(1, 4), (2, 8), (3, 24)\}$
$\{1, 2, 3\}, \{4, 8, 24\}$; yes

**4.** $\{(-1, -2), (3, 54), (-2, -16), (3, 81)\}$
$\{-2, -13\}, \{-16, -2, 54, 81\}$;
no

*Given that x is an integer, state the relation representing each of the following by listing a set of ordered pairs. Then state whether the relation is a function. Write yes or no.*

**5.** $y = 3x^2 - 5$ and $0 < x < 5$
$\{(1, -1), (2, 7), (3,22), (4,43)\}$;yes

**6.** $y^2 = 3x^2$ and $x = -3$
$\{(-3, 3\sqrt{3} -3, -3\sqrt{3})$; no

**7.** $|3y + 4| = x$ and $0 < x < 3$
$\{(1, -1),(1,- \frac{5}{3}),(2, -\frac{2}{3}),(2, -2)\}$;
no

**8.** $|y| = |x|$ and $0 < x < 2$
$\{(1, 1),(1, -1)\}$; no

*The symbol [x] means the greatest integer not greater than x. If f(x) = [2x] – 3x, find each value.*

**9.** $f(0)$
0

**10.** $f(0.5)$
$-0.5$

**11.** $f(-3.5)$
3.5

**12.** $f(x - 1)$
$[2x]-3x+1$

*Given f(x) = |3x – 4| + 5, find each value.*

**13.** $f\left(\frac{1}{3}\right)$
8

**14.** $f(0.5)$
7.5

**15.** $f(-0.5)$
10.5

**16.** $f(5d)$
$|15d-4|+5$

*Name all values of x that are not in the domain of the given function.*

**17.** $f(x) = \frac{x-2}{x+4}$
$-4$

**18.** $f(x) = \frac{1}{|2x + 5|}$
$-\frac{5}{2}$

**19.** $f(x) = \sqrt{x^2 - 25}$
$-5 < x < 5$

**20.** $f(x) = \frac{x - 10}{\sqrt{x^2 - 16}}$
$-4 \le x \le 4$

**21.** $f(x) = \frac{x^2 + 25}{x^2 - 25}$
$\pm 5$

**22.** $f(x) = \frac{x - 7}{x^2 - 1}$
$\pm 1$

Glencoe Division, Macmillan/McGraw-Hill

## 1-2 Practice Worksheet

## *Composition and Inverses of Functions*

*Given f(x) = $\frac{2}{x+4}$ and g(x) = x² − 2, find each function.*

**1.** $(f+g)(x)$  **2.** $(f-g)(x)$  **3.** $(f \cdot g)(x)$  **4.** $\left(\frac{f}{g}\right)(x)$

*Find [f ∘ g](x) and [g ∘ f](x).*

**5.** $f(x) = \frac{1}{3}x + 5$

$g(x) = x - 3$

**6.** $f(x) = 2x^3 - 3x^2 + 1$

$g(x) = 3x$

**7.** $f(x) = 2x^2 - 5x + 1$
$g(x) = 2x - 3$

**8.** $f(x) = 3x^2 - 2x + 5$
$g(x) = 2x - 1$

*Determine if the given functions are inverses of each other. Write yes or no. Show your work.*

**9.** $f(x) = 3x - 5$

$g(x) = \frac{x+5}{3}$

**10.** $f(x) = x - 10$

$g(x) = x + 10$

**11.** $f(x) = \frac{2x-3}{5}$

$g(x) = \frac{3x-5}{3}$

**12.** $f(x) = 2x$

$g(x) = \frac{2}{x}$

**13.** $f(x) = 3x - 7$

$g(x) = \frac{1}{3}x + 7$

**14.** $f(x) = 4(x+2)$

$g(x) = \frac{x}{4} - 2$

*Find the inverse of each function. Then state whether the inverse is a function.*

**15.** $f(x) = 3x + 7$  **16.** $f(x) = x^5$  **17.** $f(x) = x^2 + 4$

2

## 1-2 Practice Worksheet

# Composition and Inverses of Functions

Given $f(x) = \frac{2}{x+4}$ and $g(x) = x^2 - 2$, find each function.

**1.** $(f + g)(x)$

$\frac{x^3+4x^2-2x-6}{x+4},$

$x \neq -4$

**2.** $(f - g)(x)$

$\frac{-x^3-4x^2+2x+10}{x+4},$

$x \neq -4$

**3.** $(f \cdot g)(x)$

$\frac{2x^2-4}{x+4},$

$x \neq -4$

**4.** $\left(\frac{f}{g}\right)(x)$

$\frac{2}{(x+4)(x^2-2)},$

$x \neq -4, \pm\sqrt{2}$

**Find $[f \circ g](x)$ and $[g \circ f](x)$.**

**5.** $f(x) = \frac{1}{3}x + 5$

$g(x) = x - 3$

$\frac{1}{3}x + 4,$

$\frac{1}{3}x + 2$

**6.** $f(x) = 2x^3 - 3x^2 + 1$

$g(x) = 3x$

$54x^3 - 27x^2 + 1,$

$6x^3 - 9x^2 + 3$

**7.** $f(x) = 2x^2 - 5x + 1$
$g(x) = 2x - 3$
$8x^2 - 34x + 34,$
$4x^2 - 10x - 1$

**8.** $f(x) = 3x^2 - 2x + 5$
$g(x) = 2x - 1$
$12x^2 - 16x + 10,$
$6x^2 - 4x + 9$

**Determine if the given functions are inverses of each other. Write yes or no. Show your work.**

**9.** $f(x) = 3x - 5$

$g(x) = \frac{x+5}{3}$

**yes**

**10.** $f(x) = x - 10$

$g(x) = x + 10$

**yes**

**11.** $f(x) = \frac{2x-3}{5}$

$g(x) = \frac{3x-5}{3}$

**no**

**12.** $f(x) = 2x$

$g(x) = \frac{2}{x}$

**no**

**13.** $f(x) = 3x - 7$

$g(x) = \frac{1}{3}x + 7$

**no**

**14.** $f(x) = 4(x + 2)$

$g(x) = \frac{x}{4} - 2$

**yes**

**Find the inverse of each function. Then state whether the inverse is a function.**

**15.** $f(x) = 3x + 7$

$f^{-1}(x) = \frac{1}{3}x - \frac{7}{3}$; **yes**

**16.** $f(x) = x^5$

$f^{-1}(x) = \sqrt[5]{x}$; **yes**

**17.** $f(x) = x^2 + 4$

$f^{-1}(x) = \pm\sqrt{x-4}$;

**no**

**1-3** **Practice Worksheet**

## Linear Functions and Inequalities

*Write an inequality that describes each graph.*

**1.**

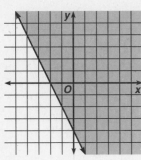

**2.**

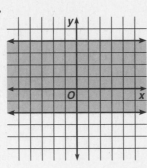

**3.**

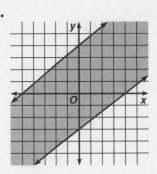

*Find the zero of each function.*

**4.** $f(x) = 0.2x + 10$

**5.** $f(x) = 11.5x$

**6.** $f(x) = 13x - 9$

**7.** $f(x) = -3$

**8.** $f(x) = -5x + 6$

**9.** $f(x) = 0.3x + 0.2$

*Graph each equation or inequality.*

**10.** $y = 3x - 2$

**11.** $1 - y = 2x$

**12.** $x \geq -2$

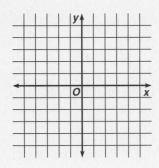

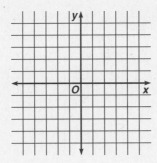

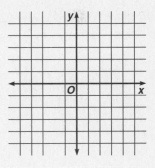

**13.** $y = |2x + 4|$

**14.** $-y > 2x + 2$

**15.** $-4 \leq x - 2y \leq 6$

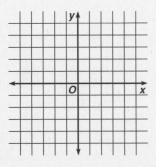

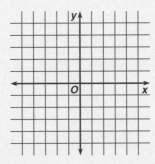

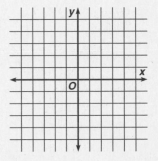

Glencoe Division, Macmillan/McGraw-Hill

# 1-3 Practice Worksheet

## Linear Functions and Inequalities

**Write an inequality that describes each graph.**

**1.**

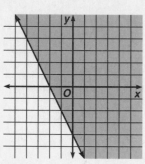

$$y \geq -2x-4$$

**2.**

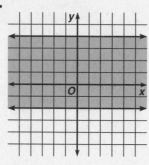

$$-2 \leq y \leq 4$$

**3.**

$$\frac{3}{4}x-3 \leq y \leq \frac{4}{5}x+4$$

**Find the zero of each function.**

**4.** $f(x) = 0.2x + 10$

$$-50$$

**5.** $f(x) = 11.5x$

$$0$$

**6.** $f(x) = 13x - 9$

$$\frac{9}{13}$$

**7.** $f(x) = -3$

**8.** $f(x) = -5x + 6$

$$\frac{6}{5}$$

**9.** $f(x) = 0.3x + 0.2$

$$-\frac{2}{3}$$

**Graph each equation or inequality.**

**10.** $y = 3x-2$

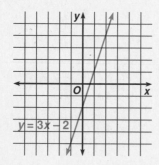

**11.** $1- y = 2x$

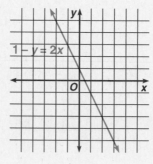

**12.** $x \geq -2$

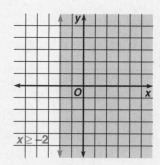

**13.** $y = |2x + 4|$

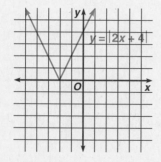

**14.** $-y > 2x + 2$

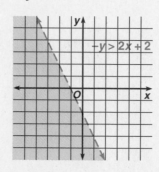

**15.** $-4 \leq x - 2y \leq 6$

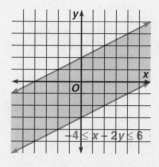

# 1-4 | Practice Worksheet

## Distance and Slope

**Find the distance between the points with the given coordinates. Then, find the slope of the line passing through each pair of points.**

**1.** $(-2, 2), (8, -3)$

**2.** $(2, -1), (7, 9)$

**3.** $(-7, 3), (5, 4)$

**4.** $(a, b + 4), (a, 2b - 5)$

**Determine whether the figure with vertices at the given points is a parallelogram.**

**5.** $(-2, 3), (-1, 7), (5, 7), (4, 3)$

**6.** $(0, 0), (3, 4), (10, 4), (0, 5)$

**7.** $(2, 3), (8, 4), (11, 9), (5, 8)$

**8.** $(-2, 3), (-8, 4), (-11, 9), (-5, 8)$

**Collinear points lie on the same line. Find the value of k for which points with each set of coordinates is collinear. (Remember, the slope of each line is constant.)**

**9.** $(2, 3), (6, k), (10, 5)$

**10.** $(k, 3), (-3, 2), (-1, 1)$

**11.** $(-3, 1), (2, 8), (7, k)$

**12.** $(-3, -3), (-1, k), (1, 19)$

**13.** Prove that the diagonals of an isosceles trapezoid are congruent using analytic methods.

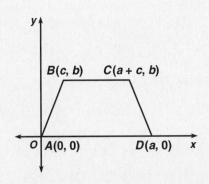

Glencoe Division, Macmillan/McGraw-Hill

## 1-4  Practice Worksheet

### Distance and Slope

**Find the distance between the points with the given coordinates. Then, find the slope of the line passing through each pair of points.**

**1.** $(-2, 2), (8, -3)$

$$5\sqrt{5}, -\frac{1}{2}$$

**2.** $(2, -1), (7, 9)$

$$5\sqrt{5}, 2$$

**3.** $(-7, 3), (5, 4)$

$$145, \frac{1}{12}$$

**4.** $(a, b + 4), (a, 2b - 5)$

$$|b - 9|, \text{undefined}$$

**Determine whether the figure with vertices at the given points is a parallelogram.**

**5.** $(-2, 3), (-1, 7), (5, 7), (4, 3)$
yes

**6.** $(0, 0), (3, 4), (10, 4), (0, 5)$
no

**7.** $(2, 3), (8, 4), (11, 9), (5, 8)$
yes

**8.** $(-2, 3), (-8, 4), (-11, 9), (-5, 8)$
yes

**Collinear points lie on the same line. Find the value of k for which points with each set of coordinates is collinear. (Remember, the slope of each line is constant.)**

**9.** $(2, 3), (6, k), (10, 5)$
4

**10.** $(k, 3), (-3, 2), (-1, 1)$
$-5$

**11.** $(-3, 1), (2, 8), (7, k)$
15

**12.** $(-3, -3), (-1, k), (1, 19)$
8

**13.** Prove that the diagonals of an isosceles trapezoid are congruent using analytic methods.

$$AC = \sqrt{((a-c) - 0)^2 + (b-0)^2}$$
$$= \sqrt{(a-c)^2 + b^2}$$
$$BD = \sqrt{(a-c)^2 + (0-b)^2}$$
$$= \sqrt{(a-c)^2 + b^2}$$

**Hence, $AC = BD$**

**So, the diagonals are congruent.**

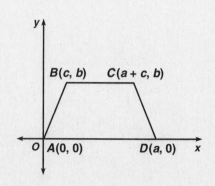

## 1-5 Practice Worksheet

### Forms of Linear Equations

**Write the slope-intercept form of the equation of the line through the point with the given coordinates and having the given slope.**

**1.** $(-3, 2), 5$            **2.** $(-1, 7), -1$

**3.** $(3, 8), -4$            **4.** $(-9, 4), \frac{4}{3}$

**5.** $(-6, 6), 1$            **6.** $(11, -11), -\frac{1}{2}$

**7.** $(2, 2), 0$            **8.** $(3, -3), -1$

**Write the slope-intercept form of the equation of the line through the points with the given coordinates.**

**9.** $(-2, 3), (1, 4)$            **10.** $(2, 5), (3, -1)$

**11.** $(0, 0), (3, -7)$            **12.** $(0, 0), (5, 7)$

**13.** $(3, 3), (6, 3)$            **14.** $(-2, -3), (-1, -3)$

**15.** $(-10, -10), (10, 23)$            **16.** $(4, 7), (7, 4)$

Glencoe Division, Macmillan/McGraw-Hill

**1-5** **Practice Worksheet**

## Forms of Linear Equations

*Write the slope-intercept form of the equation of the line through the point with the given coordinates and having the given slope.*

**1.** $(-3, 2), 5$
$$y = 5x + 17$$

**2.** $(-1, 7), -1$
$$y = -x + 6$$

**3.** $(3, 8), -4$
$$y = -4x + 20$$

**4.** $(-9, 4), \frac{4}{3}$
$$y = \frac{4}{3}x + 16$$

**5.** $(-6, 6), 1$
$$y = x + 12$$

**6.** $(11, -11), -\frac{1}{2}$
$$y = -\frac{1}{2}x = \frac{11}{2}$$

**7.** $(2, 2), 0$
$$y = 2$$

**8.** $(3, -3), -1$
$$y = -x$$

*Write the slope-intercept form of the equation of the line through the points with the given coordinates.*

**9.** $(-2, 3), (1, 4)$
$$y = \frac{1}{3}x + \frac{11}{3}$$

**10.** $(2, 5), (3, -1)$
$$y = -6x + 17$$

**11.** $(0, 0), (3, -7)$
$$y = -\frac{7}{3}x$$

**12.** $(0, 0), (5, 7)$
$$y = \frac{7}{5}x$$

**13.** $(3, 3), (6, 3)$
$$y = 3$$

**14.** $(-2, -3), (-1, -3)$
$$y = -3$$

**15.** $(-10, -10), (10, 23)$
$$y = \frac{33}{20}x + \frac{13}{2}$$

**16.** $(4, 7), (7, 4)$
$$y = -x + 11$$

Glencoe Division, Macmillan/McGraw-Hill

## 1-6 Practice Worksheet

### Parallel and Perpendicular Lines

**Write the standard form of the equation of the line that is parallel to the given line and passes through the given point.**

1. $y = -2x + 5$; $(0, 4)$

2. $y = 3x + 3$; $(-1, -2)$

3. $y = 3x + 8$; $(5, 2)$

4. $y = -x - 4$; $(6, 10)$

5. $2x - 5y = 12$; $(15, 13)$

6. $7x + 7y = 4$; $(1, 5)$

**Write the standard form of the equation of the line that is perpendicular to the given line and passes through the given point.**

7. $y = 2x + 6$; $(0, -3)$

8. $y = 7x - 9$; $(3, 4)$

9. $y = -x - 1$; $(6, 5)$

10. $2x - 5y = 6$; $(0, 9)$

11. $3x + 4y = 13$; $(2, 7)$

12. $7x + 7y = 6$; $(5, 5)$

13. For what value of $k$ is the graph of $kx + 6y - 9 = 0$ parallel to the graph of $4x - 3y - 10 = 0$? For what value of $k$ are the graphs perpendicular?

14. For what value of $k$ is the graph of $4x + ky - 7 = 0$ parallel to the graph of $3x - 4y - 10 = 0$? For what value of $k$ are the graphs perpendicular?

15. Show that the triangle with vertices $R(-3, 5)$, $S(12, 2)$, and $T(3, -4)$ is a right triangle.

Glencoe Division, Macmillan/McGraw-Hill

1-6  **Practice Worksheet**

## Parallel and Perpendicular Lines

*Write the standard form of the equation of the line that is parallel to the given line and passes through the given point.*

**1.** $y = -2x + 5$; $(0, 4)$
$2x + y - 4 = 0$

**2.** $y = 3x + 3$; $(-1, -2)$
$3x - y + 1 = 0$

**3.** $y = 3x + 8$; $(5, 2)$
$3x - y - 13 = 0$

**4.** $y = -x - 4$; $(6, 10)$
$x + y - 16 = 0$

**5.** $2x - 5y = 12$; $(15, 13)$
$2x - 5y + 35 = 0$

**6.** $7x + 7y = 4$; $(1, 5)$
$x + y - 6 = 0$

*Write the standard form of the equation of the line that is perpendicular to the given line and passes through the given point.*

**7.** $y = 2x + 6$; $(0, -3)$
$x + 2y + 6 = 0$

**8.** $y = 7x - 9$; $(3, 4)$
$x + 7y - 31 = 0$

**9.** $y = -x - 1$; $(6, 5)$
$x - y - 1 = 0$

**10.** $2x - 5y = 6$; $(0, 9)$
$5x + 2y - 18 = 0$

**11.** $3x + 4y = 13$; $(2, 7)$
$4x - 3y + 13 = 0$

**12.** $7x + 7y = 6$; $(5, 5)$
$x - y = 0$

**13.** For what value of $k$ is the graph of $kx + 6y - 9 = 0$ parallel to the graph of $4x - 3y - 10 = 0$? For what value of $k$ are the graphs perpendicular?
$-8, \dfrac{9}{2}$

**14.** For what value of $k$ is the graph of $4x + ky - 7 = 0$ parallel to the graph of $3x - 4y - 10 = 0$? For what value of $k$ are the graphs perpendicular?
$-\dfrac{16}{3}, 3$

**15.** Show that the triangle with vertices $R(-3, 5)$, $S(12, 2)$, and $T(3, -4)$ is a right triangle.
Slope $\overline{ST}$: $\dfrac{-4-2}{3-12} = \dfrac{2}{3}$; slope $\overline{RT}$: $\dfrac{5-(-4)}{-3-3} = -\dfrac{3}{2}$.

Since the slopes are negative reciprocals, $\overline{ST} \perp \overline{RT}$. Hence, $\triangle RST$ is a right triangle.

Glencoe Division, Macmillan/McGraw-Hill

# Practice Worksheet

## Solving Systems of Equations

*State whether each system is consistent and independent, consistent and dependent, or inconsistent.*

**1.** $3x + 4y = 5$
$2x - 5y = 8$

**2.** $3x - 3y = 12$
$-x + y = -4$

*Solve each system by graphing.*

**3.** $3x - y = 6$
$x + y = 6$

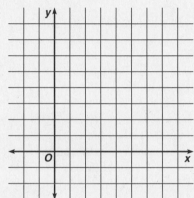

**4.** $2x + 3y = 12$
$x + y = 6$

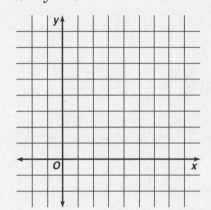

*Solve each system of equations algebraically.*

**5.** $3x - 2y = 7$
$x + y = 4$

**6.** $4x - 3y = 15$
$2x + y = 5$

**7.** $3x + 4y = 8$
$-3x - 4y = 10$

**8.** $2x - y = 6$
$x + y = 6$

**9.** $3x - 2y = -9$
$4x + 5y = 11$

**10.** $7x - y = 9$
$2x + 3y = 19$

Glencoe Division, Macmillan/McGraw-Hill

**2-1**

# Practice Worksheet

## Solving Systems of Equations

*State whether each system is consistent and independent, consistent and dependent, or inconsistent.*

**1.** $3x + 4y = 5$
$2x - 5y = 8$
**consistent and independent**

**2.** $3x - 3y = 12$
$-x + y = -4$
**consistent and dependent**

*Solve each system by graphing.*

**3.** $3x - y = 6$
$x + y = 6$

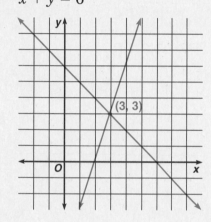

**4.** $2x + 3y = 12$
$x + y = 6$

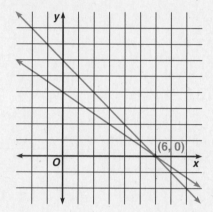

*Solve each system of equations algebraically.*

**5.** $3x - 2y = 7$
$x + y = 4$
**(3, 1)**

**6.** $4x - 3y = 15$
$2x + y = 5$
**(3, −1)**

**7.** $3x + 4y = 8$
$-3x - 4y = 10$
**no solutions**

**8.** $2x - y = 6$
$x + y = 6$
**(4, 2)**

**9.** $3x - 2y = -9$
$4x + 5y = 11$
**(−1, 3)**

**10.** $7x - y = 9$
$2x + 3y = 19$
**(2, 5)**

Glencoe Division, Macmillan/McGraw-Hill

**2-2** Practice Worksheet

## Introduction to Matrices

*Use matrices A, B, and C to find each sum, difference, or product.*

$$A = \begin{bmatrix} 2 & 3 & 1 \\ -1 & 1 & 4 \\ 5 & -2 & 3 \end{bmatrix} \quad B = \begin{bmatrix} -1 & 5 & 6 \\ 2 & -7 & -2 \\ 4 & 4 & 2 \end{bmatrix} \quad C = \begin{bmatrix} 8 & 10 & -9 \\ -6 & 12 & 14 \end{bmatrix}$$

**1.** $A + B$

**2.** $A - B$

**3.** $B - A$

**4.** $-2A$

**5.** $AB$

**6.** $AA$

**7.** $CA$

**8.** $CB$

**9.** $(CB)A$

**10.** $C(BA)$

*Find the values of x and y for which each matrix equation is true.*

**11.** $\begin{bmatrix} 2x - 3 \\ 4y \end{bmatrix} = \begin{bmatrix} y \\ 3x \end{bmatrix}$

**12.** $\begin{bmatrix} x \\ y \end{bmatrix} = \begin{bmatrix} 2y - 4 \\ 2x \end{bmatrix}$

Glencoe Division, Macmillan/McGraw-Hill

## 2-2 Practice Worksheet

### Introduction to Matrices

*Use matrices A, B, and C to find each sum, difference, or product.*

$$A = \begin{bmatrix} 2 & 3 & 1 \\ -1 & 1 & 4 \\ 5 & -2 & 3 \end{bmatrix} \quad B = \begin{bmatrix} -1 & 5 & 6 \\ 2 & -7 & -2 \\ 4 & 4 & 2 \end{bmatrix} \quad C = \begin{bmatrix} 8 & 10 & -9 \\ -6 & 12 & 14 \end{bmatrix}$$

**1.** $A + B$

$$\begin{bmatrix} 1 & 8 & 7 \\ 1 & -6 & 2 \\ 9 & 2 & 5 \end{bmatrix}$$

**2.** $A - B$

$$\begin{bmatrix} 3 & -2 & -5 \\ -3 & -8 & -6 \\ 1 & -6 & -1 \end{bmatrix}$$

**3.** $B - A$

$$\begin{bmatrix} -3 & 2 & 5 \\ 3 & -8 & -6 \\ -1 & 6 & -1 \end{bmatrix}$$

**4.** $-2A$

$$\begin{bmatrix} -4 & -6 & -2 \\ 2 & -2 & -8 \\ -10 & 4 & -6 \end{bmatrix}$$

**5.** $AB$

$$\begin{bmatrix} 8 & -7 & 8 \\ 19 & 4 & 0 \\ 3 & 51 & 40 \end{bmatrix}$$

**6.** $AA$

$$\begin{bmatrix} 6 & 7 & 17 \\ 17 & -10 & 15 \\ 27 & 7 & 6 \end{bmatrix}$$

**7.** $CA$

$$\begin{bmatrix} -39 & 52 & 21 \\ 46 & -34 & 84 \end{bmatrix}$$

**8.** $CB$

$$\begin{bmatrix} -24 & -66 & 10 \\ 86 & -58 & -32 \end{bmatrix}$$

**9.** $(CB)A$

$$\begin{bmatrix} 68 & -158 & -258 \\ 70 & 264 & -242 \end{bmatrix}$$

**10.** $C(BA)$

$$\begin{bmatrix} 68 & -158 & -258 \\ 70 & 264 & -242 \end{bmatrix}$$

*Find the values of x and y for which each matrix equation is true.*

**11.** $\begin{bmatrix} 2x - 3 \\ 4y \end{bmatrix} = \begin{bmatrix} y \\ 3x \end{bmatrix}$

$$\left( \frac{12}{5}, \frac{9}{5} \right)$$

**12.** $\begin{bmatrix} x \\ y \end{bmatrix} = \begin{bmatrix} 2y - 4 \\ 2x \end{bmatrix}$

$$\left( \frac{4}{3}, \frac{8}{3} \right)$$

Glencoe Division, Macmillan/McGraw-Hill

**2-3**

# Practice Worksheet

## *Determinants and Multiplicative Inverses of a Matrix*

### *Find the value of each determinant.*

**1.** $\begin{vmatrix} 2 & 7 \\ -3 & 5 \end{vmatrix}$

**2.** $\begin{vmatrix} 3 & -5 \\ 7 & 9 \end{vmatrix}$

**3.** $\begin{vmatrix} 2 & -1 & 3 \\ 2 & 1 & 4 \\ -3 & 1 & -2 \end{vmatrix}$

**4.** $\begin{vmatrix} 1 & -1 & 0 \\ 2 & 1 & 4 \\ 5 & -3 & 5 \end{vmatrix}$

### *Find the inverse of each matrix, if it exists.*

**5.** $\begin{bmatrix} 5 & 2 \\ 10 & 4 \end{bmatrix}$

**6.** $\begin{bmatrix} 3 & 8 \\ -1 & 5 \end{bmatrix}$

### *Solve each system by using matrix equations.*

**7.** $3x + y = 23$
$2x + y = 18$

**8.** $2x - 3y = 17$
$3x + y = 9$

**9.** $2x + 5y = 28$
$3x - 2y = -15$

**10.** $3x + 4y = 6$
$2x - 3y = 21$

**11.** $4x - 3y = -16$
$2x + 5y = 18$

**12.** $7x - 3y = 4$
$x + 2y = -14$

Glencoe Division, Macmillan/McGraw-Hill

## 2-3 Practice Worksheet

### Determinants and Multiplicative Inverses of a Matrix

**Find the value of each determinant.**

1. $\begin{vmatrix} 2 & 7 \\ -3 & 5 \end{vmatrix}$

   **31**

2. $\begin{vmatrix} 3 & -5 \\ 7 & 9 \end{vmatrix}$

   **62**

3. $\begin{vmatrix} 2 & -1 & 3 \\ 2 & 1 & 4 \\ -3 & 1 & -2 \end{vmatrix}$

   **11**

4. $\begin{vmatrix} 1 & -1 & 0 \\ 2 & 1 & 4 \\ 5 & -3 & 5 \end{vmatrix}$

   **7**

**Find the inverse of each matrix, if it exists.**

5. $\begin{bmatrix} 5 & 2 \\ 10 & 4 \end{bmatrix}$

   **does not exist**

6. $\begin{bmatrix} 3 & 8 \\ -1 & 5 \end{bmatrix}$

   $\dfrac{1}{23} \begin{bmatrix} 5 & -8 \\ 1 & 3 \end{bmatrix}$

**Solve each system by using matrix equations.**

7. $3x + y = 23$
   $2x + y = 18$
   **(5, 8)**

8. $2x - 3y = 17$
   $3x + y = 9$
   **(4, −3)**

9. $2x + 5y = 28$
   $3x - 2y = -15$
   **(−1, 6)**

10. $3x + 4y = 6$
    $2x - 3y = 21$
    **(6, −3)**

11. $4x - 3y = -16$
    $2x + 5y = 18$
    **(−1, 4)**

12. $7x - 3y = 4$
    $x + 2y = -14$
    **(−2, −6)**

Glencoe Division, Macmillan/McGraw-Hill

**2-4**

# Practice Worksheet

## Solving Systems of Equations by Using Matrices

*Solve each system of equations by using augmented matrices.*

**1.** $4x - 3y = 1$
$3x + 2y = 5$

**2.** $3x - 2y = 9$
$12x - 8y = 40$

**3.** $x + y + z = 3$
$3x - 2y - z = -4$
$x + y - z = -1$

**4.** $x + y = 5$
$3x + z = 2$
$4y - z = 8$

**5.** $4x - 3y - 6z = 2$
$2x + 3y + 3z = 2$
$10x - 6y + 3z = 0$

**6.** $3x - 5y + z = 8$
$7x + y = 4$
$4y - z = 10$

**7.** $x - y + z = 1$
$x - 2y + z = 2$
$2x - y + z = -1$

**8.** $2x - 3y - 4z = 2$
$-6x - 6y + 6z = 5$
$4x + 4y - 2z = 3$

**9.** $4x - 6y + 2z = -9$
$2x + 4y - 2z = 9$
$x - y + 3z = -4$

**10.** $x - z = 5$
$2x + y = 7$
$y + 3z = 12$

Glencoe Division, Macmillan/McGraw-Hill

## 2-4 Practice Worksheet

# Solving Systems of Equations by Using Matrices

*Solve each system of equations by using augmented matrices.*

1. $4x - 3y = 1$
   $3x + 2y = 5$
   **(1, 1)**

2. $3x - 2y = 9$
   $12x - 8y = 40$
   **(4, 1)**

3. $x + y + z = 3$
   $3x - 2y - z = -4$
   $x + y - z = -1$
   **(0, 1, 2)**

4. $x + y = 5$
   $3x + z = 2$
   $4y - z = 8$
   **(10, –5, –28)**

5. $4x - 3y - 6z = 2$
   $2x + 3y + 3z = 2$
   $10x - 6y + 3z = 0$
   $\left( \dfrac{1}{2}, \dfrac{2}{3}, -\dfrac{1}{3} \right)$

6. $3x - 5y + z = 8$
   $7x + y = 4$
   $4y - z = 10$
   **(2.2, –11.4, –55.6)**

7. $x - y + z = 1$
   $x - 2y + z = 2$
   $2x - y + z = -1$
   **(–2, –1, 2)**

8. $2x - 3y - 4z = 2$
   $-6x - 6y + 6z = 5$
   $4x + 4y - 2z = 3$
   $\left( \dfrac{13}{3}, -2, \dfrac{19}{6} \right)$

9. $4x - 6y + 2z = -9$
   $2x + 4y - 2z = 9$
   $x - y + 3z = -4$
   $\left( \dfrac{1}{2}, \dfrac{3}{2}, -1 \right)$

10. $x - z = 5$
    $2x + y = 7$
    $y + 3z = 12$
    **(20, –33, 15)**

Glencoe Division, Macmillan/McGraw-Hill

## 2-5 Practice Worksheet

### Solving Systems of Inequalities

*Solve each system of inequalities by graphing and name the coordinates of the vertices of each polygonal convex set. Then, find the maximum and minimum values for each function on that set.*

**1.** $x \geq 0$  $\quad\quad\quad$  $x + 2y \leq 6$

$y \geq 0$  $\quad\quad\quad\quad$  $f(x, y) = 2x - y$

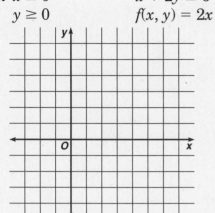

**2.** $x \geq 0$  $\quad\quad\quad$  $2x + 3y \leq 12$

$y \geq 0$  $\quad\quad\quad\quad$  $f(x, y) = 2x + 3y$

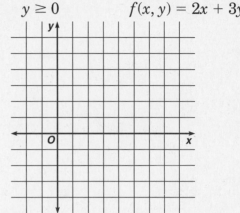

**3.** $x \geq 0$  $\quad\quad\quad$  $5x + 6y \leq 18$

$y + 2 \geq 0$  $\quad\quad\quad$  $f(x, y) = 2x + 3y$

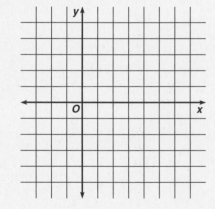

**4.** $x \geq 0$  $\quad\quad\quad$  $y \geq x - 4$

$y \geq 0$  $\quad\quad\quad\quad$  $f(x, y) = 3x - 5y$

$7x + 6y \leq 54$

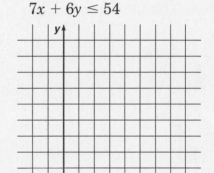

**5.** $y \leq -x + 8$  $\quad\quad$  $4x - 3y \geq -3$

$x + 8y \geq 8$  $\quad\quad$  $f(x, y) = 4x - 5y$

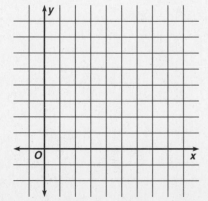

**6.** $3x - 2y \geq 0$  $\quad$  $y \geq 0$

$3x + 2y \leq 24$  $\quad$  $f(x, y) = 7y - 3x$

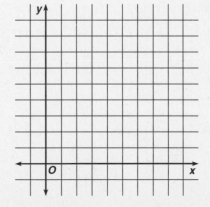

Glencoe Division, Macmillan/McGraw-Hill

2-5  **Practice Worksheet**

## Solving Systems of Inequalities

*Solve each system of inequalities by graphing and name the coordinates of the vertices of each polygonal convex set. Then, find the maximum and minimum values for each function on that set.*

**1.** $x \geq 0$       $x + 2y \leq 6$
    $y \geq 0$       $f(x, y) = 2x - y$

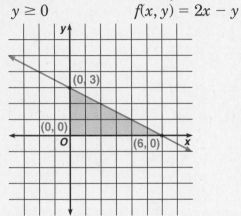

max=12, min=−3

**2.** $x \geq 0$       $2x + 3y \leq 12$
    $y \geq 0$       $f(x, y) = 2x + 3y$

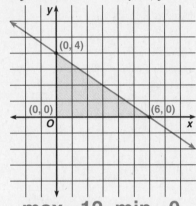

max=12, min=0

**3.** $x \geq 0$       $5x + 6y \leq 18$
    $y + 2 \geq 0$     $f(x, y) = 2x + 3y$

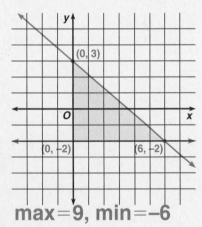

max=9, min=−6

**4.** $x \geq 0$       $y \geq x - 4$
    $y \geq 0$       $f(x, y) = 3x - 5y$
    $7x + 6y \leq 54$

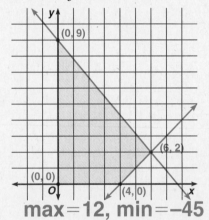

max=12, min=−45

**5.** $y \leq -x + 8$     $4x - 3y \geq -3$
    $x + 8y \geq 8$      $f(x, y) = 4x - 5y$

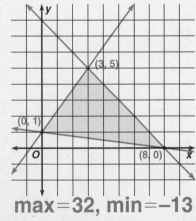

max=32, min=−13

**6.** $3x - 2y \geq 0$     $y \geq 0$
    $3x + 2y \leq 24$    $f(x, y) = 7y - 3x$

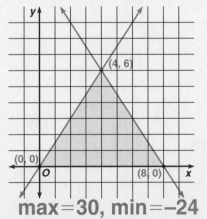

max=30, min=−24

Glencoe Division, Macmillan/McGraw-Hill

2-6

# Practice Worksheet

## Linear Programming

*Solve each problem, if possible. If not possible, state whether the problem is infeasible, has alternate optional solutions, or is unbounded.*

1. Toys-A-Go makes toys at Plant A and Plant B. Plant A has materials to make up to 1000 toy dump trucks and fire engines. Plant B has materials to make up to 800 toy dump trucks and fire engines. Plant A can make 10 toy dump trucks and 5 toy fire engines per hour. Plant B can produce 5 toy dump trucks and 15 toy fire engines per hour. It costs $300 per hour to operate Plant A and $350 to operate Plant B per hour. How many hours should each plant be run in order to minimize cost?

2. Roadster Skateboard makes skateboards at Plants X and Y. Plant X must make at least 720 standard and deluxe boards. Plant Y has materials to make up to 520 standard and deluxe boards. Plant X can make 12 standard and 5 deluxe boards per hour. Plant Y can make 10 standard and 8 deluxe boards per hour. It costs $250 to operate Plant X per hour and $225 to operate Plant Y per hour. How many hours should each plant be run in order to minimize cost?

Glencoe Division, Macmillan/McGraw-Hill

## 2-6 Practice Worksheet

### Linear Programming

*Solve each problem, if possible. If not possible, state whether the problem is infeasible, has alternate optional solutions, or is unbounded.*

1. Toys-A-Go makes toys at Plant A and Plant B. Plant A has materials to make up to 1000 toy dump trucks and fire engines. Plant B has materials to make up to 800 toy dump trucks and fire engines. Plant A can make 10 toy dump trucks and 5 toy fire engines per hour. Plant B can produce 5 toy dump trucks and 15 toy fire engines per hour. It costs $300 per hour to operate Plant A and $350 to operate Plant B per hour. How many hours should each plant be run in order to minimize cost?

   **Plant A: 88 hours**
   **Plant B: 24 hours**
   **minimum cost = $34,800**

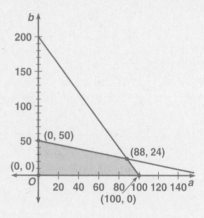

2. Roadster Skateboard makes skateboards at Plants X and Y. Plant X must make at least 720 standard and deluxe boards. Plant Y has materials to make up to 520 standard and deluxe boards. Plant X can make 12 standard and 5 deluxe boards per hour. Plant Y can make 10 standard and 8 deluxe boards per hour. It costs $250 to operate Plant X per hour and $225 to operate Plant Y per hour. How many hours should each plant be run in order to minimize cost?

   **infeasible**

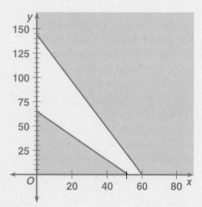

Glencoe Division, Macmillan/McGraw-Hill

## 3-1 Practice Worksheet

### Symmetry

**Find the coordinates of P′ if P and P′ are symmetric with respect to point M.**

**1.** $P(-7, 4)$, $M(0, 0)$

**2.** $P(5, 4)$, $M(-3, 2)$

**3.** $P(-5, 5)$, $M(10, 12)$

**The graphs below are portions of complete graphs. Sketch a complete graph for each of the following symmetries: with respect to (a) the x-axis, (b) the y-axis, (c) the line y = x, and (d) the line y = –x.**

**4.**

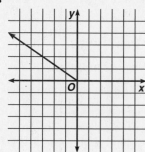

**5.**

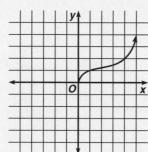

**6.**

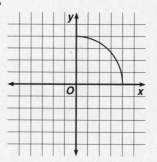

**Determine if each function is an even function, an odd function, or neither.**

**7.** $y = x^2 + x - 2$

**8.** $y = \sqrt{4x^2 - 25}$

**9.** $y = -2x^7 + x^5 - x^3$

**Determine whether the graph of each equation is symmetric with respect to the origin, the x-axis, the y-axis, the line y = x, or the line y = –x.**

**10.** $xy = -12$

**11.** $y = \pm\sqrt{x + 6}$

**12.** $y^2 = \dfrac{x^2}{9} - 16$

Glencoe Division, Macmillan/McGraw-Hill

**3-1** | # Practice Worksheet

## Symmetry

**Find the coordinates of P′ if P and P′ are symmetric with respect to point M.**

**1.** $P(-7, 4)$, $M(0, 0)$
**(7, −4)**

**2.** $P(5, 4)$, $M(-3, 2)$
**(−11, 0)**

**3.** $P(-5, 5)$, $M(10, 12)$
**(25, 19)**

**The graphs below are portions of complete graphs. Sketch a complete graph for each of the following symmetries: with respect to (a) the x-axis, (b) the y-axis, (c) the line y = x, and (d) the line y = −x.**

**4.**
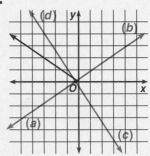

**5.**
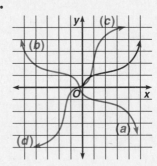

**6.**
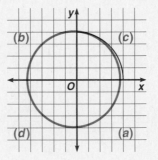

**Determine if each function is an even function, an odd function, or neither.**

**7.** $y = x^2 + x - 2$
**neither**

**8.** $y = \sqrt{4x^2 - 25}$
**even**

**9.** $y = -2x^7 + x^5 - x^3$
**odd**

**Determine whether the graph of each equation is symmetric with respect to the origin, the x-axis, the y-axis, the line y = x, or the line y = −x.**

**10.** $xy = -12$

$y = x$, **origin**

**11.** $y = \pm \sqrt{x + 6}$

**x–axis**

**12.** $y^2 = \frac{x^2}{9} - 16$

**x–axis, y–axis, origin**

Glencoe Division, Macmillan/McGraw-Hill

# 3-2 Practice Worksheet

## Families of Graphs

*The graph of f(x) is shown. Sketch a graph of each function based on the graph of f(x).*

**1.**

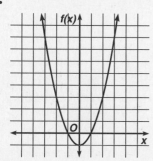

**a.** $g(x) = -2f(x)$

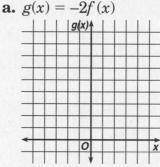

**b.** $h(x) = 2f(x)$

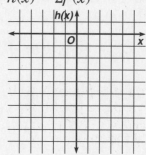

**2.**

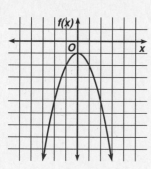

**a.** $g(x) = -2f(x) + 1$

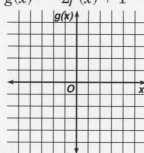

**b.** $h(x) = 2f(-x)$

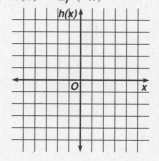

*For each parent graph, describe the transformation(s) that have taken place in the related graph of each function.*

**3.** $f(x) = x^2$
   **a.** $y = 2x^2$

   **b.** $y = -0.5(x - 2)^2$

   **c.** $y = 3x^2 + 1$

**4.** $f(x) = [x]$
   **a.** $y = 3[x] - 1$

   **b.** $y = 0.5[x] - 1$

   **c.** $y = [-x]$

*Sketch the graph of each function.*

**5.** $f(x) = -(x - 1)^2 + 1$

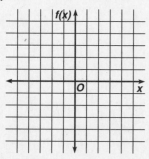

**6.** $f(x) = 2|x + 2| - 3$

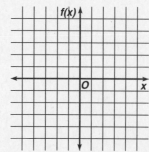

**14**

Glencoe Division, Macmillan/McGraw-Hill

## 3-2

# Practice Worksheet

## Families of Graphs

*The graph of f(x) is shown. Sketch a graph of each function based on the graph of f(x).*

**1.**

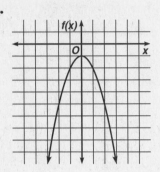

**a.** $g(x) = -2f(x)$

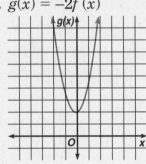

**b.** $h(x) = 2f(x)$

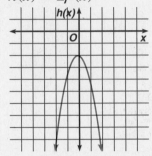

**2.**

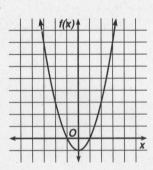

**a.** $g(x) = -2f(x) + 1$

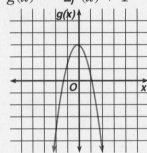

**b.** $h(x) = 2f(-x)$

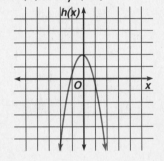

*For each parent graph, describe the transformation(s) that have taken place in the related graph of each function.*

**3.** $f(x) = x^2$
 **a.** $y = 2x^2$
 **vertical stretch**
 **b.** $y = -0.5(x - 2)^2$ **vertical shrink, reflect over x–axis, move 2 units right**
 **c.** $y = 3x^2 + 1$ **vertical stretch, translation 1 unit up**

**4.** $f(x) = [x]$
 **a.** $y = 3[x] - 1$ **vertical stretch, translation 1 unit down**
 **b.** $y = 0.5[x] - 1$ **vertical shrink, translation 1 unit down**
 **c.** $y = [-x]$ **reflection over the y–axis**

*Sketch the graph of each function.*

**5.** $f(x) = -(x - 1)^2 + 1$

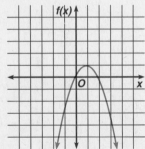

**6.** $f(x) = 2|x + 2| - 3$

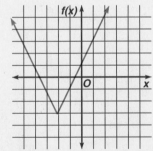

3-3 **Practice Worksheet**

## Inverse Functions and Relations

**Find the inverse of each function.**

**1.** $y = -5x + 7$

**2.** $y = -4x^2 + 1$

**Find the inverse of each function. Sketch the function and its inverse. Is the inverse a function? Write yes or no.**

**3.** $y = (x - 1)^3 + 1$

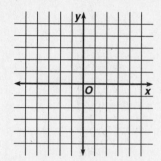

**4.** $y = 4x^2 - 1$

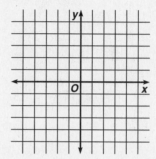

**5.** $y = 4(x + 1)^2 - 2$

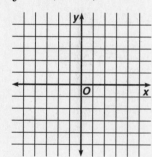

**6.** $y = \sqrt[3]{x - 1}$

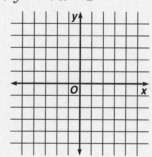

**For the parent graph $f(x) = x^2$, describe the transformation(s) that have taken place in the related graph of each function.**

**7.** $y = \pm \sqrt{x - 1}$

**8.** $y = \pm \sqrt{x} + 1$

**9.** $y = \pm 2\sqrt{x}$

**10.** $y = \pm 2\sqrt{x - 1}$

Glencoe Division, Macmillan/McGraw-Hill

**3-3** **Practice Worksheet**

## Inverse Functions and Relations

*Find the inverse of each function.*

**1.** $y = -5x + 7$

$$y = \frac{-x + 7}{5}$$

**2.** $y = -4x^2 + 1$

$$y = \pm \frac{1}{2} \sqrt{1-x}$$

*Find the inverse of each function. Sketch the function and its inverse. Is the inverse a function? Write yes or no.*

**3.** $y = (x-1)^3 + 1$   $y = \sqrt[3]{x-1} + 1$; **yes**

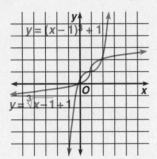

**4.** $y = 4x^2 - 1$   $y = \pm \frac{1}{2} \sqrt{1-x}$; **no**

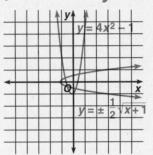

**5.** $y = 4(x+1)^2 - 2$   $y = \pm \frac{1}{2} \sqrt{x+2} - 1$; **no**

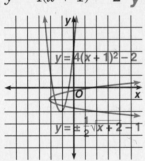

**6.** $y = \sqrt[3]{x-1}$   $y = x^3 + 1$; **yes**

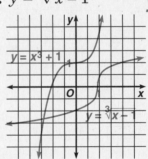

*For the parent graph $f(x) = x^2$, describe the transformation(s) that have taken place in the related graph of each function.*

**7.** $y = \pm \sqrt{x-1}$
**translates the inverse 1 unit to the right**

**8.** $y = \pm \sqrt{x} + 1$
**translates the inverse 1 unit up**

**9.** $y = \pm 2\sqrt{x}$
**vertically stretches the inverse**

**10.** $y = \pm 2\sqrt{x-1}$
**translates the inverse 1 unit to the right; then vertically stretches the graph**

Glencoe Division, Macmillan/McGraw-Hill

NAME _____ DATE _____

# Practice Worksheet

## Rational Functions and Asymptotes

*Determine any horizontal, vertical, or slant asymptotes in the graph of each function.*

**1.** $y = \dfrac{x}{x^2 + 2x + 1}$
 **2.** $y = \dfrac{x - 1}{x^5 - 4x^3}$
 **3.** $y = \dfrac{5x^2 - 10x + 1}{x - 2}$

*For each parent graph, describe the transformation(s) that have taken place in the related graph of each function. Then sketch the graph.*

**4.** $f(x) = \dfrac{1}{x}$

  **a.** $y = \dfrac{4}{x}$

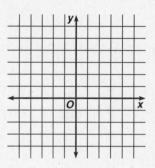

  **b.** $y = \dfrac{1}{x - 1} - 1$

*Create a function of the form y = f(x) that satisfies each set of conditions.*

**5.** vertical asymptote at $x = 1$, hole at $x = 0$

**6.** holes at $x = -1$ and $x = 0$, resembles $y = x^2$

*Graph each rational function.*

**7.** $y = \dfrac{x + 3}{x - 2}$
 **8.** $y = \dfrac{x^2 + 2x - 3}{x - 1}$

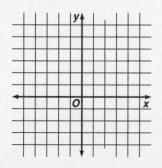
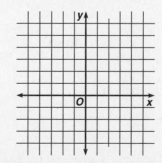

Glencoe Division, Macmillan/McGraw-Hill

**3-4**

# Practice Worksheet

## Rational Functions and Asymptotes

*Determine any horizontal, vertical, or slant asymptotes in the graph of each function.*

**1.** $y = \dfrac{x}{x^2 + 2x + 1}$

vertical: $x = -1$
horizontal: $y = 0$

**2.** $y = \dfrac{x - 1}{x^5 - 4x^3}$

vertical: $x = 0, 2$
horizontal: $y = 0$

**3.** $y = \dfrac{5x^2 - 10x + 1}{x - 2}$

vertical: $x = z$
slant: $y = 5x$

*For each parent graph, describe the transformation(s) that have taken place in the related graph of each function. Then sketch the graph.*

**4.** $f(x) = \dfrac{1}{x}$    The graph of $y = \dfrac{4}{x}$ does not come

**a.** $y = \dfrac{4}{x}$    as close to the origin as the graph

of $y = \dfrac{1}{x}$. The vertical asymptote is still

$x = 0$ and the horizontal asymptote is

still $y = 0$.

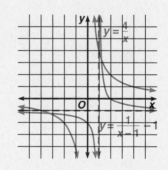

**b.** $y = \dfrac{1}{x - 1} - 1$

The graph of $y = \dfrac{1}{x}$ is translated 1 unit
to the right and 1 unit down. The new
vertical asymptote is $x = 1$ and the
horizontal asymptote is $y = 1$.

*Create a function of the form y = f(x) that satisfies each set of conditions.*

**5.** vertical asymptote at $x = 1$, hole at $x = 0$

$y = \dfrac{x}{x^2 - x}$

**6.** holes at $x = -1$ and $x = 0$, resembles $y = x^2$

$y = \dfrac{x^4 + x^3}{x^2 + x}$

*Graph each rational function.*

**7.** $y = \dfrac{x + 3}{x - 2}$

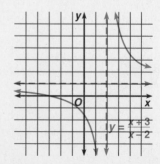

**8.** $y = \dfrac{x^2 + 2x - 3}{x - 1}$

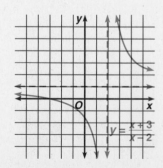

Glencoe Division, Macmillan/McGraw-Hill

## 3-5 | **Practice Worksheet**

### *Graphs of Inequalities*

**Graph each inequality.**

**1.** $y > -2x + 1$

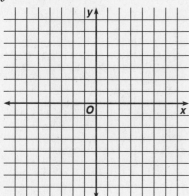

**2.** $y < 2|x - 1|$

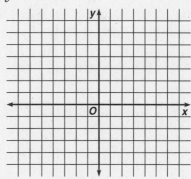

**3.** $y > (x - 1)^2$

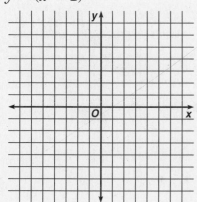

**4.** $y > \pm \sqrt{x + 1}$

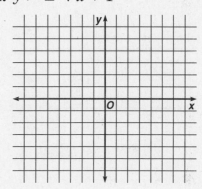

**Solve each inequality.**

**5.** $|2x + 5| > 3$

**6.** $|3x - 10| \le 5$

**7.** $|4x - 10| \le 6$

**8.** $|2x - 7| > 8$

**9.** $|-x + 1| > -1$

**10.** $|2x + 5| < 0$

## 3-5 Practice Worksheet

## *Graphs of Inequalities*

*Graph each inequality.*

**1.** $y > -2x + 1$

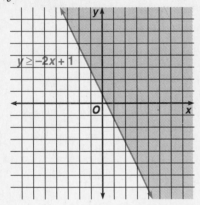

**2.** $y < 2|x - 1|$

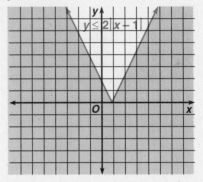

**3.** $y > (x - 1)^2$

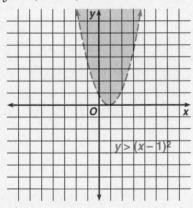

**4.** $y > \pm\sqrt{x + 1}$

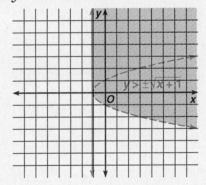

*Solve each inequality.*

**5.** $|2x + 5| > 3$

$\{x | x < -4 \text{ or } x > -1\}$

**6.** $|3x - 10| \le 5$

$\{x | \frac{5}{3} \le x \le 5\}$

**7.** $|4x - 10| \le 6$

$\{x | 1 \le x \le 4\}$

**8.** $|2x - 7| > 8$

$\{x | x < -\frac{1}{2} \text{ or } x > \frac{15}{2}\}$

**9.** $|-x + 1| > -1$
**all real numbers**

**10.** $|2x + 5| < 0$
$\varnothing$

Glencoe Division, Macmillan/McGraw-Hill

## 3-6 **Practice Worksheet**

### *Tangent to a Curve*

*Find the derivative of each function.*

**1.** $f(x) = 1.2x^4 - 3.5x^3 + 2.4x$

**2.** $f(x) = 3x^{-3} - 5x^{-2} - 4x$

**3.** $f(x) = \dfrac{2}{x^5} - \dfrac{5}{x^2}$

**4.** $f(x) = \dfrac{1}{3}x^3 + \dfrac{1}{2}x^2 + 3$

*Find the slope of the line tangent to the graph of each function at the given point.*

**5.** $y = 3x^2$, $(1, 3)$

**6.** $y = \dfrac{1}{2} x^2 - 4$, $(2, -2)$

**7.** $y = \dfrac{4x^3 - 7}{2}$ , $(1, 0)$

*Find the equation of the line tangent to the graph of each function at the given point. Write the equation in slope-intercept form. Graph the function and the tangent.*

**8.** $y = 2x^2 - 1$, $(-1, 1)$

**9.** $y = x^2 - 5x + 1$, $(0, 1)$

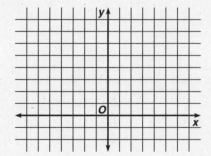
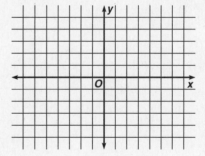

**10.** Find the coordinates of the point(s) at which the line tangent to the graph of $f(x) = x^2 - 1$ has slope –2.

**3-6**

# Practice Worksheet

## Tangent to a Curve

**Find the derivative of each function.**

**1.** $f(x) = 1.2x^4 - 3.5x^3 + 2.4x$

$$4.8\ x^3 - 10.5x^2 + 2.4$$

**2.** $f(x) = 3x^{-3} - 5x^{-2} - 4x$

$$-9x^{-4} + 10x^{-3} - 4$$

**3.** $f(x) = \frac{2}{x^5} - \frac{5}{x^2}$

$$-10x^{-6} + 10x^{-3}$$

**4.** $f(x) = \frac{1}{3}x^3 + \frac{1}{2}x^2 + 3$

$$x^2 + x$$

**Find the slope of the line tangent to the graph of each function at the given point.**

**5.** $y = 3x^2$, $(1, 3)$

$$6$$

**6.** $y = \frac{1}{2}x^2 - 4$, $(2, -2)$

$$2$$

**7.** $y = \frac{4x^3 - 7}{2}$, $(1, 0)$

$$6$$

**Find the equation of the line tangent to the graph of each function at the given point. Write the equation in slope-intercept form. Graph the function and the tangent.**

**8.** $y = 2x^2 - 1$, $(-1, 1)$

$$y = -4x - 3$$

**9.** $y = x^2 - 5x + 1$, $(0, 1)$

$$y = -5x + 1$$

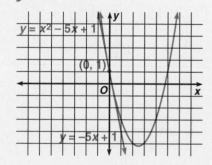

**10.** Find the coordinates of the point(s) at which the line tangent to the graph of $f(x) = x^2 - 1$ has slope $-2$.

$$(-1, 0)$$

Glencoe Division, Macmillan/McGraw-Hill

**3-7**

# Practice Worksheet

## Graphs and Critical Points of Polynomial Functions

*Find the critical points for each function. Then determine whether each point is a minimum, a maximum, or a point of inflection.*

**1.** $f(x) = x^2 - 6x + 1$

**2.** $f(x) = 2x^2 - 10x + 3$

**3.** $f(x) = -3x^2 + 9x$

**4.** $f(x) = -x^2 + 5x - 1$

**5.** $f(x) = x^3 + x^2 - x$

**6.** $f(x) = x^4 - 10x^2 + 9$

*Find the x- and y-intercepts of the graph of each function.*

**7.** $f(x) = 2x^2 + 5x - 3$

**8.** $f(x) = x^2 - 10x + 21$

**9.** $f(x) = (x + 1)(x - 1)(x + 2)$

**10.** $f(x) = x^3 + 5x^2 + 6x$

**11.** $f(x) = (x - 2)^3$

**12.** $f(x) = x^4 + 2x^2 + 1$

**13.** Graph $f(x) = 2x^3 + 3x$.

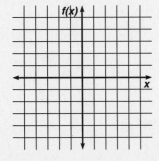

Glencoe Division, Macmillan/McGraw-Hill

**3-7**

# Practice Worksheet

## Graphs and Critical Points of Polynomial Functions

*Find the critical points for each function. Then determine whether each point is a minimum, a maximum, or a point of inflection.*

**1.** $f(x) = x^2 - 6x + 1$

   **(3, −8), min**

**2.** $f(x) = 2x^2 - 10x + 3$

   $\left(\dfrac{5}{2}, -\dfrac{19}{2}\right)$, **min**

**3.** $f(x) = -3x^2 + 9x$

   $\left(\dfrac{3}{2}, \dfrac{27}{4}\right)$, **max**

**4.** $f(x) = -x^2 + 5x - 1$

   $\left(\dfrac{5}{2}, \dfrac{21}{4}\right)$ **max**

**5.** $f(x) = x^3 + x^2 - x$

   **(−1,1), max**

   $\left(\dfrac{1}{3}, -\dfrac{5}{27}\right)$, **min**

**6.** $f(x) = x^4 - 10x^2 + 9$

   **(−$\sqrt{5}$, −16), min**

   **(0, 9), max**

   **($\sqrt{5}$, −16), min**

*Find the x- and y-intercepts of the graph of each function.*

**7.** $f(x) = 2x^2 + 5x - 3$

   **x–intercepts: −3, $\dfrac{1}{2}$**

   **y–intercept: −3**

**8.** $f(x) = x^2 - 10x + 21$

   **x–intercepts: 3,7**

   **y–intercept: 21**

**9.** $f(x) = (x + 1)(x - 1)(x + 2)$

   **x–intercepts: −2, −1, 1**
   **y–intercept: −2**

**10.** $f(x) = x^3 + 5x^2 + 6x$

   **x–intercepts: −3, −2, 0**
   **y–intercept: 0**

**11.** $f(x) = (x - 2)^3$

   **x–intercept: 2**
   **y–intercept: −8**

**12.** $f(x) = x^4 + 2x^2 + 1$

   **x–intercepts: none**
   **y–intercept: 1**

**13.** Graph $f(x) = 2x^3 + 3x$.

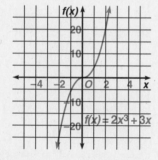

Glencoe Division, Macmillan/McGraw-Hill

# 3-8 Practice Worksheet

## Continuity and End Behavior

*Determine whether each graph has infinite discontinuity, jump discontinuity, or point discontinuity, or is continuous. Then graph each function.*

**1.** $y = \dfrac{2}{3x^2}$

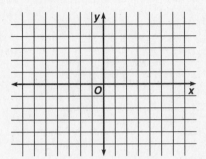

**2.** $y = \dfrac{x^2 - 1}{x + 1}$

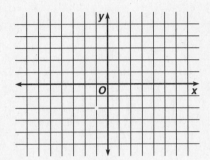

**3.** $y = \dfrac{|x|^2}{x}$

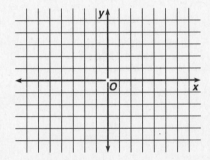

**4.** $y = 2x^2 - 4x + 1$

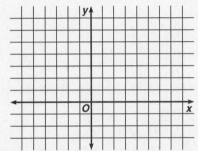

**5.** $y = x^3 - 2x + 2$

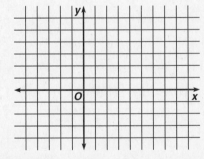

**6.** $y = \begin{cases} 2x + 1, & \text{if } x < 0 \\ 2x + 2, & \text{if } x > 0 \end{cases}$

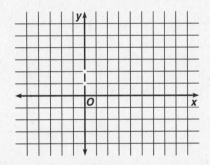

*Without graphing, describe the end behavior of each function.*

**7.** $y = 2x^5 - 4x$

**8.** $y = -x^2 + 13$

**9.** $y = 6 - 6x - 6x^3$

**10.** $y = x^3 + 2x - 1$

**11.** $y = x^2 - 49$

**12.** $y = x^4 + x^3 + x^2 + x$

Glencoe Division, Macmillan/McGraw-Hill

## 3-8 Practice Worksheet

### Continuity and End Behavior

*Determine whether each graph has infinite discontinuity, jump discontinuity, or point discontinuity, or is continuous. Then graph each function.*

**1.** $y = \frac{2}{3x^2}$   **infinite discontinuity**

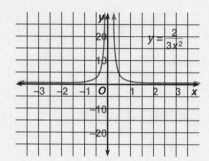

**2.** $y = \frac{x^2 - 1}{x + 1}$   **point discontinuity**

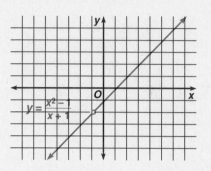

**3.** $y = \frac{|x|^2}{x}$   **point discontinuity**

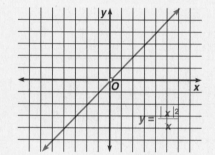

**4.** $y = 2x^2 - 4x + 1$   **continuous**

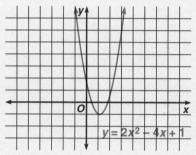

**5.** $y = x^3 - 2x + 2$   **continuous**

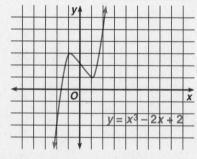

**6.** $y = \begin{cases} 2x + 1, & \text{if } x < 0 \\ 2x + 2, & \text{if } x > 0 \end{cases}$   **jump discontinuity**

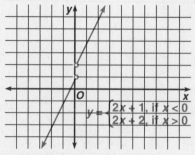

*Without graphing, describe the end behavior of each function.*

**7.** $y = 2x^5 - 4x$
as $x \to -\infty$, $y \to -\infty$
as $x \to \infty$, $y \to \infty$

**8.** $y = -x^2 + 13$
as $x \to -\infty$, $y \to -\infty$
as $x \to \infty$, $y \to -\infty$

**9.** $y = 6 - 6x - 6x^3$
as $x \to -\infty$, $y \to \infty$
as $x \to \infty$, $y \to -\infty$

**10.** $y = x^3 + 2x - 1$
as $x \to -\infty$, $y \to -\infty$
as $x \to \infty$, $y \to \infty$

**11.** $y = x^2 - 49$
as $x \to -\infty$, $y \to \infty$
as $x \to \infty$, $y \to \infty$

**12.** $y = x^4 + x^3 + x^2 + x$
as $x \to -\infty$, $y \to \infty$
as $x \to \infty$, $y \to \infty$

Glencoe Division, Macmillan/McGraw-Hill

**4-1** **Practice Worksheet**

## Polynomial Functions

*State the number of complex roots of each equation. Then find the roots and graph the related function.*

**1.** $3x - 5 = 0$

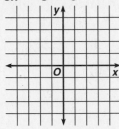

**2.** $x^2 + 4 = 0$

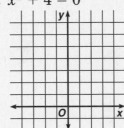

**3.** $c^2 + 2c + 1 = 0$

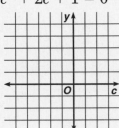

**4.** $x^3 + 2x^2 - 15x = 0$

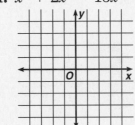

*Write the polynomial equation of least degree for each set of roots given.*

**5.** $4, 0.5$

**6.** $3, -0.5, 1$

**7.** $3, 3, 1, 1, -2$

**8.** $1 \pm 2i, 3$

**9.** $\pm 2i, 3, -3$

**10.** $-1, 3 \pm i, 2 \pm 3i$

*Solve each equation and graph the related function.*

**11.** $x^3 + 6x + 20 = 0$

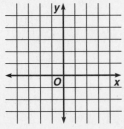

**12.** $x^4 + 5x^3 + 9x^2 + 45x = 0$

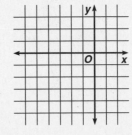

Glencoe Division, Macmillan/McGraw-Hill

# Practice Worksheet

## Polynomial Functions

**State the number of complex roots of each equation. Then find the roots and graph the related function.**

**1.** $3x - 5 = 0$

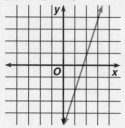

one; $\dfrac{5}{3}$

**2.** $x^2 + 4 = 0$

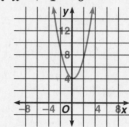

two; $\pm\, 2i$

**3.** $c^2 + 2c + 1 = 0$

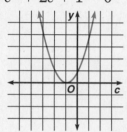

two; $-1$ and $-1$

**4.** $x^3 + 2x^2 - 15x = 0$

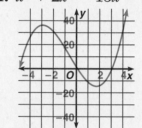

three; $-5, 0, 3$

**Write the polynomial equation of least degree for each set of roots given.**

**5.** $4, 0.5$

$2x^2 - 9x + 4 = 0$

**6.** $3, -0.5, 1$

$2x^3 - 7x^2 + 2x + 3 = 0$

**7.** $3, 3, 1, 1, -2$

$x^5 - 6x^4 + 6x^3 + 20x^2 - 39x + 18 = 0$

**8.** $1 \pm 2i, 3$

$x^3 - 5x^2 + 11x - 15$

**9.** $\pm\, 2i, 3, -3$

$x^4 - 5x^2 - 36 = 0$

**10.** $-1, 3 \pm i, 2 \pm 3i$

$x^5 - 9x^4 + 37x^3 - 71x^2 + 12x + 130 = 0$

**Solve each equation and graph the related function.**

**11.** $x^3 + 6x + 20 = 0$

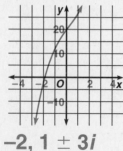

$-2, 1 \pm 3i$

**12.** $x^4 + 5x^3 + 9x^2 + 45x = 0$

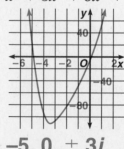

$-5, 0, \pm\, 3i$

Glencoe Division, Macmillan/McGraw-Hill

# 4-2 Practice Worksheet

## Quadratic Equations and Inequalities

*Solve each equation by completing the square. Then graph the related function.*

**1.** $x^2 - 4x + 7 = 0$

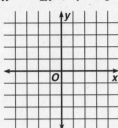

**2.** $-4x^2 - 8x = 7$

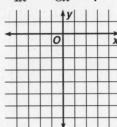

*Find the discriminant of each equation and describe the nature of the roots of the equation. Then solve each equation by using the quadratic formula and graph the related function.*

**3.** $x^2 + x - 6 = 0$

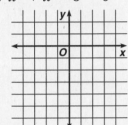

**4.** $-2x^2 + x - 5 = 0$

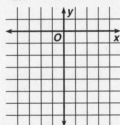

*Graph each quadratic inequality.*

**5.** $y > x^2 - 4x - 5$

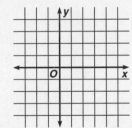

**6.** $y < 4x^2 - 4x - 15$

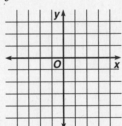

**7.** $y \geq 8x^2 - 14x - 15$

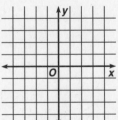

*Determine the critical point(s) of the graph of each function to the nearest tenth. State if the point is a relative maximum, a relative minimum, or a point of inflection.*

**8.** $f(x) = 2x^3 - 3x^2 - 36x + 6$

**9.** $f(x) = x^3 - 3x + 3$

Glencoe Division, Macmillan/McGraw-Hill

# Practice Worksheet

## Quadratic Equations and Inequalities

Solve each equation by completing the square. Then graph the related function.

**1.** $x^2 - 4x + 7 = 0$

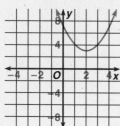

$$2 \pm i\sqrt{3}$$

**2.** $-4x^2 - 8x = 7$

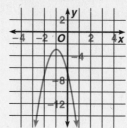

$$-1 \pm \frac{\sqrt{3}}{2}i$$

Find the discriminant of each equation and describe the nature of the roots of the equation. Then solve each equation by using the quadratic formula and graph the related function.

**3.** $x^2 + x - 6 = 0$

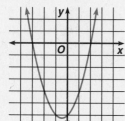

25, two real; –3, 2

**4.** $-2x^2 + x - 5 = 0$

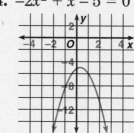

–39, two complex; $\dfrac{-1 \pm \sqrt{39}i}{-4}$

Graph each quadratic inequality.

**5.** $y > x^2 - 4x - 5$

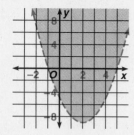

**6.** $y < 4x^2 - 4x - 15$

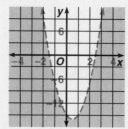

**7.** $y \geq 8x^2 - 14x - 15$

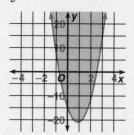

Determine the critical point(s) of the graph of each function to the nearest tenth. State if the point is a relative maximum, a relative minimum, or a point of inflection.

**8.** $f(x) = 2x^3 - 3x^2 - 36x + 6$
(–2, 50); relative maximum
(3, –75); relative minimum

**9.** $f(x) = x^3 - 3x + 3$
(–1, 5); relative maximum
(1, 1); relative minimum

Glencoe Division, Macmillan/McGraw-Hill

4-3

# Practice Worksheet

## The Remainder and Factor Theorems

**Divide using synthetic division.**

1. $(x^2 - 5x - 12) \div (x + 3)$

2. $(3x^2 + 4x - 12) \div (x - 5)$

3. $(2x^3 + 3x^2 - 8x + 3) \div (x + 3)$

4. $(x^4 - 3x^2 + 1) \div (x - 1)$

**Find the remainder for each division. Is the divisor a factor of the polynomial?**

5. $(2x^3 - 3x^2 - 10x + 3) \div (x - 3)$

6. $(2x^4 + 4x^3 - x^2 + 9) \div (x + 2)$

7. $(10x^3 - x^2 + 8x + 29) \div \left(x + \frac{2}{5}\right)$

8. $(2x^4 + 14x^3 - 2x^2 - 14x) \div (x + 7)$

**Use the remainder theorem to find the remainder for each division. State whether the binomial is a factor of the polynomial.**

9. $(3x^3 - 2x^2 + x - 4) \div (x - 2)$

10. $(x^4 - x^3 - 10x^2 + 4x + 24) \div (x + 2)$

11. $(x^4 + 5x^3 - 14x^2) \div (x + 7)$

12. $(x^3 + x^2 - 10) \div (x + 3)$

**Find the value of k so that each remainder is zero.**

13. $(2x^3 + kx^2 + 7x - 3) \div (x - 3))$

14. $(x^3 + 9x^2 + kx - 12) \div (x + 4)$

15. Determine how many times 2 is a root of $x^3 - 7x^2 + 16x - 12 = 0$.

Glencoe Division, Macmillan/McGraw-Hill

## 4-3 Practice Worksheet

## The Remainder and Factor Theorems

**Divide using synthetic division.**

**1.** $(x^2 - 5x - 12) \div (x + 3)$
$x - 8, R\ 12$

**2.** $(3x^2 + 4x - 12) \div (x - 5)$
$3x + 19, R\ 83$

**3.** $(2x^3 + 3x^2 - 8x + 3) \div (x + 3)$
$2x^2 - 3x + 1$

**4.** $(x^4 - 3x^2 + 1) \div (x - 1)$
$x^3 + x^2 - 2x - 2, R\ -1$

**Find the remainder for each division. Is the divisor a factor of the polynomial?**

**5.** $(2x^3 - 3x^2 - 10x + 3) \div (x - 3)$
$0,\ yes$

**6.** $(2x^4 + 4x^3 - x^2 + 9) \div (x + 2)$
$5,\ no$

**7.** $(10x^3 - x^2 + 8x + 29) \div \left(x + \dfrac{2}{5}\right)$

$25,\ no$

**8.** $(2x^4 + 14x^3 - 2x^2 - 14x) \div (x + 7)$

$0,\ yes$

**Use the remainder theorem to find the remainder for each division. State whether the binomial is a factor of the polynomial.**

**9.** $(3x^3 - 2x^2 + x - 4) \div (x - 2)$
$14,\ no$

**10.** $(x^4 - x^3 - 10x^2 + 4x + 24) \div (x + 2)$
$0,\ yes$

**11.** $(x^4 + 5x^3 - 14x^2) \div (x + 7)$
$0,\ yes$

**12.** $(x^3 + x^2 - 10) \div (x + 3)$
$-28,\ no$

**Find the value of k so that each remainder is zero.**

**13.** $(2x^3 + kx^2 + 7x - 3) \div (x - 3))$
$-8$

**14.** $(x^3 + 9x^2 + kx - 12) \div (x + 4)$
$17$

**15.** Determine how many times 2 is a root of $x^3 - 7x^2 + 16x - 12 = 0$.
twice

NAME _____ DATE _____

# Practice Worksheet

## The Rational Root Theorem

*List all possible rational zeros of each function. Then determine the rational zeros.*

**1.** $f(x) = x^3 + 3x^2 - 6x - 8$

**2.** $f(x) = 36x^4 - 13x^2 + 1$

**3.** $f(x) = x^3 - 9x^2 + 27x - 27$

**4.** $f(x) = x^3 - x^2 - 8x + 12$

**5.** $f(x) = x^4 - 3x^3 - 11x^2 + 3x + 10$

**6.** $f(x) = 5x^4 - 2x - 4$

**7.** $f(x) = 3x^5 - 7x^2 + x + 6$

**8.** $f(x) = x^3 + 4x^2 - 2x + 15$

**9.** $f(x) = 2x^3 - 3x^2 - 2x + 3$

**10.** $f(x) = 4x^3 - 8x^2 + x + 3$

*Find the number of possible positive real zeros and the number of possible negative real zeros. Determine all of the rational zeros.*

**11.** $f(x) = 3x^3 + 7x^2 + 2x + 4$

**12.** $f(x) = 5x^4 - 3x^2 + x - 7$

**13.** $f(x) = x^4 - 2x^3 - 4x^2 + 11x - 6$

**14.** $f(x) = x^4 - 4x^3 - 7x^2 + 34x - 24$

**15.** $f(x) = 3x^3 - 4x^2 - 17x + 6$

**16.** $f(x) = 2x^3 + 3x^2 + 5x + 2$

Glencoe Division, Macmillan/McGraw-Hill

## 4-4 | Practice Worksheet

# The Rational Root Theorem

**List all possible rational zeros of each function. Then determine the rational zeros.**

**1.** $f(x) = x^3 + 3x^2 - 6x - 8$

$\{\pm 1, \pm 2, \pm 4, \pm 8\};\ -4, -1, 2$

**2.** $f(x) = 36x^4 - 13x^2 + 1$

$\left\{\pm\dfrac{1}{36}, \pm\dfrac{1}{18}, \pm\dfrac{1}{12}, \pm\dfrac{1}{9}, \pm\dfrac{1}{6},\right.$

$\left.\pm\dfrac{1}{4}, \pm\dfrac{1}{3}, \pm\dfrac{1}{2}, \pm 1\right\};\ \pm\dfrac{1}{2}, \pm\dfrac{1}{3}$

**3.** $f(x) = x^3 - 9x^2 + 27x - 27$

$\{\pm 1, \pm 3, \pm 9, \pm 27\};\ 3$

**4.** $f(x) = x^3 - x^2 - 8x + 12$

$\{\pm 1, \pm 2, \pm 3, \pm 4, \pm 6, \pm 12\};$
$-3, 2$

**5.** $f(x) = x^4 - 3x^3 - 11x^2 + 3x + 10$

$\{\pm 1, \pm 2, \pm 5, \pm 10\};\ \pm 1, -2, 5$

**6.** $f(x) = 5x^4 - 2x - 4$

$\left\{\pm 1, \pm 2, \pm 4, \pm\dfrac{1}{5}, \pm\dfrac{2}{5}, \pm\dfrac{4}{5}\right\};$
none

**7.** $f(x) = 3x^5 - 7x^2 + x + 6$

$\left\{\pm 1, \pm 2, \pm 3, \pm 6, \pm\dfrac{1}{3}, \pm\dfrac{2}{3}\right\};$
none

**8.** $f(x) = x^3 + 4x^2 - 2x + 15$

$\{\pm 1, \pm 3, \pm 5, \pm 15\};\ -5$

**9.** $f(x) = 2x^3 - 3x^2 - 2x + 3$

$\left\{\pm 1, \pm 3, \pm\dfrac{1}{2}, \pm\dfrac{3}{2}\right\};\ \pm 1, \dfrac{3}{2}$

**10.** $f(x) = 4x^3 - 8x^2 + x + 3$

$\left\{\pm 1, \pm 3, \pm\dfrac{1}{4}, \pm\dfrac{1}{2}, \pm\dfrac{3}{4}, \pm\dfrac{3}{2}\right\};$

$1, -\dfrac{1}{2}, \dfrac{3}{2}$

**Find the number of possible positive real zeros and the number of possible negative real zeros. Determine all of the rational zeros.**

**11.** $f(x) = 3x^3 + 7x^2 + 2x + 4$

0, 3 or 1; none

**12.** $f(x) = 5x^4 - 3x^2 + x - 7$

3 or 1; 1; none

**13.** $f(x) = x^4 - 2x^3 - 4x^2 + 11x - 6$

3 or 1; 1; $\left\{1, 2, \dfrac{-1 \pm \sqrt{13}}{2}\right\}$

**14.** $f(x) = x^4 - 4x^3 - 7x^2 + 34x - 24$

3 or 1; 1; $\{-3, 1, 2, 4\}$

**15.** $f(x) = 3x^3 - 4x^2 - 17x + 6$

2 or 0; 1; $\left\{-2, \dfrac{1}{3}, 3\right\}$

**16.** $f(x) = 2x^3 + 3x^2 + 5x + 2$

0, 3 or 1; $\left\{-\dfrac{1}{2}\right\}$

Glencoe Division, Macmillan/McGraw-Hill

4-5 | **Practice Worksheet**

## Locating the Zeros of a Function

***Determine between which consecutive integers the real zeros of each function are located.***

1. $f(x) = 2x^3 - 7x^2 + 4x + 3$

2. $f(x) = 2x^3 - 13x^2 + 14x - 4$

3. $f(x) = 2x^3 - 13x^2 + 43x - 14$

4. $f(x) = 2x^3 - 7x^2 + 12x - 9$

5. $f(x) = 4x^4 - 16x^3 - 25x^2 + 196x - 146$

6. $f(x) = x^3 - 3$

***Approximate the real zeros of each function to the nearest tenth.***

7. $f(x) = 4x^4 + 2x^2 - 1$

8. $f(x) = x^3 - 2x + 2$

9. $f(x) = x^4 - 5x^2 + 1$

10. $f(x) = 2x^3 + x^2 - 1$

11. $f(x) = x^3 - 2x^2 - 2x$

12. $f(x) = x^3 - 5x^2 + 4$

***Use the upper bound theorem to find the least integral upper bound and the greatest integral lower bound of the zeros of each function.***

13. $f(x) = 2x^3 - x^2 + x - 6$

14. $f(x) = x^4 + x^2 - 3$

15. $f(x) = x^3 + 3x + 7$

16. $f(x) = 2x^4 - x^3 - 6x^2 - 2x - 30$

17. For $f(x) = x^3 - 3x^2$, determine the number and type of possible complex zeros. Use the location principle to determine the zeros to the nearest tenth. Determine the relative maxima and relative minima. Then, sketch the graph.

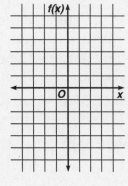

# 4-5 Practice Worksheet

## Locating the Zeros of a Function

**Determine between which consecutive integers the real zeros of each function are located.**

**1.** $f(x) = 2x^3 - 7x^2 + 4x + 3$
**−1 and 0; 1 and 2; 2 and 3**

**2.** $f(x) = 2x^3 - 13x^2 + 14x - 4$
**5 and 6**

**3.** $f(x) = 2x^3 - 13x^2 + 43x - 14$
**0 and 1**

**4.** $f(x) = 2x^3 - 7x^2 + 12x - 9$
**1 and 2**

**5.** $f(x) = 4x^4 - 16x^3 - 25x^2 + 196x - 146$
**−4 and 3; 0 and 1**

**6.** $f(x) = x^3 - 3$
**1 and 2**

**Approximate the real zeros of each function to the nearest tenth.**

**7.** $f(x) = 4x^4 + 2x^2 - 1$
**± 0.6**

**8.** $f(x) = x^3 - 2x + 2$
**−1.8**

**9.** $f(x) = x^4 - 5x^2 + 1$
**± 2.2, ± 0.5**

**10.** $f(x) = 2x^3 + x^2 - 1$
**0.7**

**11.** $f(x) = x^3 - 2x^2 - 2x$
**−0.7, 0, 2.7**

**12.** $f(x) = x^3 - 5x^2 + 4$
**−0.8, 1, 4.8**

**Use the upper bound theorem to find the least integral upper bound and the greatest integral lower bound of the zeros of each function.**

**13.** $f(x) = 2x^3 - x^2 + x - 6$
**2, −1**

**14.** $f(x) = x^4 + x^2 - 3$
**2, −2**

**15.** $f(x) = x^3 + 3x + 7$
**1, −2**

**16.** $f(x) = 2x^4 - x^3 - 6x^2 - 2x - 30$
**3, −3**

**17.** For $f(x) = x^3 - 3x^2$, determine the number and type of possible complex zeros. Use the location principle to determine the zeros to the nearest tenth. Determine the relative maxima and relative minima. Then, sketch the graph.

**three real roots: 3 and 0 twice;**
**(0, 0) relative maximum**
**(2, −4) relative minimum**

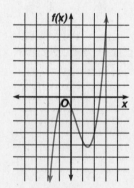

Glencoe Division, Macmillan/McGraw-Hill

**4-6**

# Practice Worksheet

## Rational Equations and Partial Fractions

**Solve each equation. Check your solution.**

**1.** $c - \frac{4}{c} = 3$

**2.** $\frac{1}{2n} + \frac{6n - 9}{3n} = \frac{2}{n}$

**3.** $\frac{4}{x - 3} + \frac{3}{x} = \frac{-2x}{x - 3}$

**4.** $\frac{15}{s} - s + 8 = 10$

**5.** $1 - \frac{2m}{m - 3} = \frac{1}{m + 3}$

**6.** $\frac{3}{d + 5} + \frac{2}{d - 1} = 1$

**Solve each inequality.**

**7.** $\frac{6}{t} + 3 > \frac{2}{t}$

**8.** $\frac{2n + 1}{3n + 1} < \frac{n - 1}{3n + 1}$

**9.** $1 + \frac{3y}{y - 1} > 2$

**10.** $\frac{2x}{4} - \frac{5x + 1}{3} > 3$

**Decompose each expression into partial fractions.**

**11.** $\frac{-3x - 29}{x^2 - 4x - 21}$

**12.** $\frac{7x^2 - 12x + 11}{2x^3 - 5x^2 + x + 2}$

**13.** Solve $\frac{x - 5}{x^2 - 5x + 6} > 0$.

Glencoe Division, Macmillan/McGraw-Hill

## 4-6 Practice Worksheet

## Rational Equations and Partial Fractions

**Solve each equation. Check your solution.**

**1.** $c - \frac{4}{c} = 3$

$-1, 4$

**2.** $\frac{1}{2n} + \frac{6n - 9}{3n} = \frac{2}{n}$

$\frac{9}{4}$

**3.** $\frac{4}{x - 3} + \frac{3}{x} = \frac{-2x}{x - 3}$

$-\frac{9}{2}, 1$

**4.** $\frac{15}{s} - s + 8 = 10$

$-5, 3$

**5.** $1 - \frac{2m}{m - 3} = \frac{1}{m + 3}$

$-6, -1$

**6.** $\frac{3}{d + 5} + \frac{2}{d - 1} = 1$

$-3, 4$

**Solve each inequality.**

**7.** $\frac{6}{t} + 3 > \frac{2}{t}$

$t < -\frac{4}{3}$ or $t > 0$

**8.** $\frac{2n + 1}{3n + 1} < \frac{n - 1}{3n + 1}$

$-2 < n < -\frac{1}{3}$

**9.** $1 + \frac{3y}{y - 1} > 2$

$y < -\frac{1}{2}$ or $y > 1$

**10.** $\frac{2x}{4} - \frac{5x + 1}{3} > 3$

$x < -\frac{20}{7}$

**Decompose each expression into partial fractions.**

**11.** $\frac{-3x - 29}{x^2 - 4x - 21}$

$-\frac{5}{x - 7} + \frac{2}{x + 3}$

**12.** $\frac{7x^2 - 12x + 11}{2x^3 - 5x^2 + x + 2}$

$\frac{3}{x - 2} - \frac{2}{x - 1} + \frac{5}{2x + 1}$

**13.** Solve $\frac{x - 5}{x^2 - 5x + 6} > 0$.

$2 < x < 3$ or $x > 5$

Glencoe Division, Macmillan/McGraw-Hill

# 4-7 Practice Worksheet

## Radical Equations and Inequalities

**Solve each equation. Check your solution.**

**1.** $\sqrt{4x + 9} - 3 = 5$

**2.** $\sqrt{1 - 7y} = 3$

**3.** $\sqrt[4]{2x - 9} = 2$

**4.** $\sqrt[3]{7v + 5} = -3$

**5.** $\sqrt{7 + x} - 5 = \sqrt{6 - x}$

**6.** $\sqrt{5 + x} - \sqrt{x - 3} = 2$

**7.** $\sqrt{x + 1} = 3 - \sqrt{4 - x}$

**8.** $\sqrt{x^2 - 2x + 1} = 2x + 5$

**Solve each inequality. Check your solution.**

**9.** $\sqrt{2z - 3} < 5$

**10.** $\sqrt{3x + 5} > 1$

**11.** $\sqrt{3x + 5} < 9$

**12.** $\sqrt{2x + 3} > 5$

**13.** Solve $2\sqrt{x} = \sqrt{4x - 3} + 1$. Check your solution.

Glencoe Division, Macmillan/McGraw-Hill

## 4-7 Practice Worksheet

## Radical Equations and Inequalities

**Solve each equation. Check your solution.**

**1.** $\sqrt{4x + 9} - 3 = 5$
$\dfrac{55}{4}$

**2.** $\sqrt{1 - 7y} = 3$
$-\dfrac{8}{7}$

**3.** $\sqrt[4]{2x - 9} = 2$
$\dfrac{25}{2}$

**4.** $\sqrt[3]{7v + 5} = -3$
$-\dfrac{32}{7}$

**5.** $\sqrt{7 + x} - 5 = \sqrt{6 - x}$
**no real solutions**

**6.** $\sqrt{5 + x} - \sqrt{x - 3} = 2$
**4**

**7.** $\sqrt{x + 1} = 3 - \sqrt{4 - x}$
**0, 3**

**8.** $\sqrt{x^2 - 2x + 1} = 2x + 5$
$-\dfrac{4}{3}$

**Solve each inequality. Check your solution.**

**9.** $\sqrt{2z - 3} < 5$
$\dfrac{3}{2} \le z \le 14$

**10.** $\sqrt{3x + 5} > 1$
$x > -\dfrac{4}{3}$

**11.** $\sqrt{3x + 5} < 9$
$-\dfrac{5}{3} < x < \dfrac{76}{3}$

**12.** $\sqrt{2x + 3} > 5$
$x \ge 11$

**13.** Solve $2\sqrt{x} = \sqrt{4x - 3} + 1$. Check your solution.
**1**

Glencoe Division, Macmillan/McGraw-Hill

# 5-1 | Practice Worksheet

## Angles and Their Measure

**If each angle has the given measure and is in standard position, determine the quadrant in which its terminal side lies.**

1. $\frac{7\pi}{12}$          2. $-\frac{2\pi}{3}$          3. $371°$          4. $\frac{14\pi}{5}$

5. $-156°$          6. $1000°$          7. $332°$          8. $-240°$

**Change each degree measure to radian measure in terms of $\pi$.**

9. $36°$          10. $-250°$          11. $-145°$          12. $6°$

13. $870°$          14. $18°$          15. $-820°$          16. $345°$

**Change each radian measure to degree measure.**

17. $-1$          18. $4\pi$          19. $-2.56$          20. $12.85$

21. $\frac{3\pi}{16}$          22. $-\frac{7\pi}{9}$          23. $\frac{13\pi}{30}$          24. $-\frac{17\pi}{3}$

**Find one positive angle and one negative angle that are coterminal with each angle.**

25. $70°$          26. $-\frac{2\pi}{5}$          27. $-300°$          28. $\frac{3\pi}{4}$

**Find the reference angle for each angle with the given measure.**

29. $-20°$          30. $160°$          31. $-545°$          32. $300°$

33. $\frac{10\pi}{3}$          34. $-\frac{5\pi}{8}$          35. $-\frac{\pi}{4}$          36. $-\frac{7\pi}{3}$

Glencoe Division, Macmillan/McGraw-Hill

## 5-1  Practice Worksheet

### Angles and Their Measure

*If each angle has the given measure and is in standard position, determine the quadrant in which its terminal side lies.*

1. $\frac{7\pi}{12}$
II

2. $-\frac{2\pi}{3}$
III

3. $371°$
I

4. $\frac{14\pi}{5}$
II

5. $-156°$
III

6. $1000°$
IV

7. $332°$
IV

8. $-240°$
II

*Change each degree measure to radian measure in terms of $\pi$.*

9. $36°$
$\frac{\pi}{5}$

10. $-250°$
$-\frac{25\pi}{18}$

11. $-145°$
$-\frac{29\pi}{36}$

12. $6°$
$\frac{\pi}{30}$

13. $870°$
$\frac{87\pi}{18}$

14. $18°$
$\frac{\pi}{10}$

15. $-820°$
$-\frac{41\pi}{9}$

16. $345°$
$\frac{23\pi}{12}$

*Change each radian measure to degree measure.*

17. $-1$
$-57°$

18. $4\pi$
$720°$

19. $-2.56$
$-147°$

20. $12.85$
$736°$

21. $\frac{3\pi}{16}$
$33.75°$

22. $-\frac{7\pi}{9}$
$-140°$

23. $\frac{13\pi}{30}$
$78°$

24. $-\frac{17\pi}{3}$
$-1020°$

## 25–28 Answers may vary. Sample answers are given.

*Find one positive angle and one negative angle that are coterminal with each angle.*

25. $70°$
$430°, \ -290°$

26. $-\frac{2\pi}{5}$
$\frac{8\pi}{5}, -\frac{12\pi}{5}$

27. $-300°$
$60°, -660°$

28. $\frac{3\pi}{4}$
$\frac{11\pi}{4}, -\frac{5\pi}{4}$

*Find the reference angle for each angle with the given measure.*

29. $-20°$
$20°$

30. $160°$
$20°$

31. $-545°$
$5°$

32. $300°$
$60°$

33. $\frac{10\pi}{3}$
$\frac{\pi}{3}$

34. $-\frac{5\pi}{8}$
$\frac{3\pi}{8}$

35. $-\frac{\pi}{4}$
$\frac{\pi}{4}$

36. $-\frac{7\pi}{3}$
$\frac{\pi}{3}$

Glencoe Division, Macmillan/McGraw-Hill

NAME _____ DATE _____

# Practice Worksheet

## Central Angles and Arcs

**Given the radian measure of a central angle, find the measure of its intercepted arc in terms of $\pi$ in a circle of radius 10 cm.**

**1.** $\frac{\pi}{6}$            **2.** $\frac{\pi}{3}$            **3.** $\frac{\pi}{2}$            **4.** $\frac{\pi}{5}$

**5.** $\frac{3\pi}{5}$            **6.** $\frac{4\pi}{7}$            **7.** $\frac{\pi}{12}$            **8.** $\frac{\pi}{24}$

**Given the measurement of a central angle, find the measure of its intercepted arc in terms of $\pi$ in a circle of diameter 60 in.**

**9.** $10°$            **10.** $60°$            **11.** $42°$            **12.** $50°$

**13.** $72°$            **14.** $110°$            **15.** $35°$            **16.** $65°$

**Given the measure of an arc, find the degree measure to the nearest tenth of the central angle it subtends in a circle of radius 16 cm.**

**17.** $87$            **18.** $5.6$            **19.** $12$            **20.** $25$

**21.** $10.24$            **22.** $7.9$            **23.** $11$            **24.** $6$

**Find the area of each sector to the nearest tenth, given its central angle, $\theta$, and the radius of the circle.**

**25.** $\theta = \frac{\pi}{6}$ , $r = 14$ cm            **26.** $\theta = \frac{\pi}{6}$ , $r = 12$ ft

Glencoe Division, Macmillan/McGraw-Hill

**5-2**

# Practice Worksheet

## Central Angles and Arcs

*Given the radian measure of a central angle, find the measure of its intercepted arc in terms of $\pi$ in a circle of radius 10 cm.*

**1.** $\frac{\pi}{6}$

$\frac{5\pi}{3}$ cm

**2.** $\frac{\pi}{3}$

$\frac{10\pi}{3}$ cm

**3.** $\frac{\pi}{2}$

$5\pi$ cm

**4.** $\frac{\pi}{5}$

$2\pi$ cm

**5.** $\frac{3\pi}{5}$

$6\pi$ cm

**6.** $\frac{4\pi}{7}$

$\frac{40\pi}{7}$ cm

**7.** $\frac{\pi}{12}$

$\frac{5\pi}{6}$ cm

**8.** $\frac{\pi}{24}$

$\frac{5\pi}{12}$ cm

*Given the measurement of a central angle, find the measure of its intercepted arc in terms of $\pi$ in a circle of diameter 60 in.*

**9.** $10°$

$\frac{5\pi}{3}$ in.

**10.** $60°$

$10\pi$ in.

**11.** $42°$

$7\pi$ in.

**12.** $50°$

$\frac{25\pi}{3}$ in.

**13.** $72°$

$12\pi$ in.

**14.** $110°$

$\frac{55\pi}{3}$ in.

**15.** $35°$

$\frac{35\pi}{6}$ in.

**16.** $65°$

$\frac{65\pi}{6}$ in.

*Given the measure of an arc, find the degree measure to the nearest tenth of the central angle it subtends in a circle of radius 16 cm.*

**17.** $87$
$311.5°$

**18.** $5.6$
$20.1°$

**19.** $12$
$43.0°$

**20.** $25$
$89.5°$

**21.** $10.24$
$36.7°$

**22.** $7.9$
$28.3°$

**23.** $11$
$39.4°$

**24.** $6$
$21.5°$

*Find the area of each sector to the nearest tenth, given its central angle, $\theta$, and the radius of the circle.*

**25.** $\theta = \frac{\pi}{6}$, $r = 14$ cm

$51.3$ cm$^2$

**26.** $\theta = \frac{\pi}{6}$, $r = 12$ ft

$37.7$ ft$^2$

Glencoe Division, Macmillan/McGraw-Hill

## 5-3   **Practice Worksheet**

### *Circular Functions*

*Find the values of the six trigonometric functions of an angle in standard position if the given point lies on its terminal side.*

**1.** $(-1, 5)$          **2.** $(6, -8)$          **3.** $(3, 2)$          **4.** $(-3, -4)$

**5.** $(0, -4)$          **6.** $(7, 0)$          **7.** $(\sqrt{2}, -\sqrt{2})$          **8.** $\left(\frac{\sqrt{3}}{2}, -\frac{1}{2}\right)$

*Suppose $\theta$ is an angle in standard position whose terminal side lies in the given quadrant. For each function, find the values of the remaining five trigonometric functions of $\theta$.*

**9.** $\cos \theta = \frac{3}{5}$ ; quadrant I          **10.** $\sin \theta = -\frac{2}{3}$ ; quadrant IV

Glencoe Division, Macmillan/McGraw-Hill

# 5-3 Practice Worksheet

## Circular Functions

**Find the values of the six trigonometric functions of an angle in standard position if the given point lies on its terminal side.**

**1.** $(-1, 5)$

$\sin \theta = \dfrac{5\sqrt{26}}{26}$

$\cos \theta = -\dfrac{\sqrt{26}}{26}$

$\tan \theta = -5$

$\csc \theta = \dfrac{\sqrt{26}}{5}$

$\sec \theta = -\sqrt{26}$

$\cot \theta = -\dfrac{1}{5}$

**2.** $(6, -8)$

$\sin \theta = -\dfrac{4}{5}$

$\cos \theta = \dfrac{3}{5}$

$\tan \theta = -\dfrac{4}{3}$

$\csc \theta = -\dfrac{5}{4}$

$\sec \theta = \dfrac{5}{3}$

$\cot \theta = -\dfrac{3}{4}$

**3.** $(3, 2)$

$\sin \theta = \dfrac{2\sqrt{13}}{13}$

$\cos \theta = \dfrac{3\sqrt{13}}{13}$

$\tan \theta = \dfrac{2}{3}$

$\csc \theta = \dfrac{\sqrt{13}}{2}$

$\sec \theta = \dfrac{\sqrt{13}}{3}$

$\cot \theta = \dfrac{3}{2}$

**4.** $(-3, -4)$

$\sin \theta = -\dfrac{4}{5}$

$\cos \theta = -\dfrac{3}{5}$

$\tan \theta = \dfrac{4}{3}$

$\csc \theta = -\dfrac{5}{4}$

$\sec \theta = -\dfrac{5}{3}$

$\cot \theta = \dfrac{3}{4}$

**5.** $(0, -4)$

$\sin \theta = -1$

$\cos \theta = 0$

$\tan \theta$ : undefined

$\csc \theta = -1$

$\sec \theta$ : undefined

$\cot \theta = 0$

**6.** $(7, 0)$

$\sin \theta = 0$

$\cos \theta = 1$

$\tan \theta = 0$

$\csc \theta$ : undefined

$\sec \theta = 1$

$\cot \theta$ : undefined

**7.** $(\sqrt{2}, -\sqrt{2})$

$\sin \theta = -\dfrac{\sqrt{2}}{2}$

$\cos \theta = \dfrac{\sqrt{2}}{2}$

$\tan \theta = -1$

$\csc \theta = -\sqrt{2}$

$\sec \theta = \sqrt{2}$

$\cot \theta = -1$

**8.** $\left(\dfrac{\sqrt{3}}{2}, -\dfrac{1}{2}\right)$

$\sin \theta = -\dfrac{1}{2}$

$\cos \theta = \dfrac{\sqrt{3}}{2}$

$\tan \theta = -\dfrac{\sqrt{3}}{3}$

$\csc \theta = -2$

$\sec \theta = \dfrac{2\sqrt{3}}{3}$

$\cot \theta = -\sqrt{3}$

**Suppose $\theta$ is an angle in standard position whose terminal side lies in the given quadrant. For each function, find the values of the remaining five trigonometric functions of $\theta$.**

**9.** $\cos \theta = \dfrac{3}{5}$ ; quadrant I

$\sin \theta = \dfrac{4}{5}$; $\tan \theta = \dfrac{4}{3}$

$\csc \theta = \dfrac{5}{4}$; $\sec \theta = \dfrac{5}{3}$

$\cot \theta = \dfrac{3}{4}$

**10.** $\sin \theta = -\dfrac{2}{3}$ ; quadrant IV

$\cos \theta = \dfrac{\sqrt{5}}{3}$; $\tan \theta = -\dfrac{2\sqrt{5}}{5}$;

$\csc \theta = -\dfrac{3}{2}$; $\sec \theta = \dfrac{3\sqrt{5}}{5}$

$\cot \theta = -\dfrac{\sqrt{5}}{2}$

Glencoe Division, Macmillan/McGraw-Hill

## 5-4 Practice Worksheet

## Trigonometric Functions of Special Angles

**Find each exact value. Do not use a calculator.**

**1.** $\sin \frac{\pi}{4}$

**2.** $\cos \frac{\pi}{4}$

**3.** $\tan \frac{\pi}{4}$

**4.** $\cos 210°$

**5.** $\sin 300°$

**6.** $\tan 330°$

**7.** $\sin \frac{3\pi}{4}$

**8.** $\cos \frac{3\pi}{4}$

**9.** $\tan \frac{3\pi}{4}$

**10.** $\sin 90°$

**11.** $\csc 270°$

**12.** $\tan 45°$

**13.** $\cos \frac{3\pi}{2}$

**14.** $\tan \frac{3\pi}{2}$

**15.** $\sin \frac{3\pi}{2}$

**Use a calculator to approximate each value to four decimal places.**

**16.** $\cot (-75°)$

**17.** $\sin 634°$

**18.** $\cos 235°$

**19.** $\sin 2$

**20.** $\sec 4.28$

**21.** $\cot 0.23$

Glencoe Division, Macmillan/McGraw-Hill

**5-4**

# Practice Worksheet

## Trigonometric Functions of Special Angles

**Find each exact value. Do not use a calculator.**

**1.** $\sin \frac{\pi}{4}$

$\frac{\sqrt{2}}{2}$

**2.** $\cos \frac{\pi}{4}$

$\frac{\sqrt{2}}{2}$

**3.** $\tan \frac{\pi}{4}$

**1**

**4.** $\cos 210°$

$-\frac{\sqrt{3}}{2}$

**5.** $\sin 300°$

$-\frac{\sqrt{3}}{2}$

**6.** $\tan 330°$

$-\frac{\sqrt{3}}{3}$

**7.** $\sin \frac{3\pi}{4}$

$\frac{\sqrt{2}}{2}$

**8.** $\cos \frac{3\pi}{4}$

$-\frac{\sqrt{2}}{2}$

**9.** $\tan \frac{3\pi}{4}$

$-1$

**10.** $\sin 90°$
**1**

**11.** $\csc 270°$
$-1$

**12.** $\tan 45°$
**1**

**13.** $\cos \frac{3\pi}{2}$

**0**

**14.** $\tan \frac{3\pi}{2}$

**undefined**

**15.** $\sin \frac{3\pi}{2}$

$-1$

**Use a calculator to approximate each value to four decimal places.**

**16.** $\cot (-75°)$
$-0.2679$

**17.** $\sin 634°$
$-0.9976$

**18.** $\cos 235°$
$-0.5736$

**19.** $\sin 2$
$0.9093$

**20.** $\sec 4.28$
$-2.3864$

**21.** $\cot 0.23$
$4.2709$

Glencoe Division, Macmillan/McGraw-Hill

## 5-5 Practice Worksheet

### Right Triangles

*Solve each triangle described, given the triangle below. Round angle measures to the nearest degree and side measures to the nearest tenth.*

**1.** $A = 39°12'$, $b = 2.1$

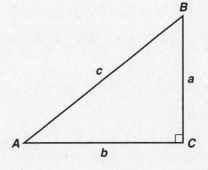

**2.** $a = 9$, $B = 49°$

**3.** $B = 64°$, $b = 19.2$        **4.** $B = 56°48'$, $c = 63.1$

**5.** $A = 16°$, $c = 14$        **6.** $a = 0.4$, $c = 0.5$

**7.** $c = 21.3$, $A = 26°20'$        **8.** $a = 2$, $b = 7$

**9.** $A = 55°55'$, $c = 16$        **10.** $a = \sqrt{15}$, $B = 18°$

Glencoe Division, Macmillan/McGraw-Hill

**5-5**  ## Practice Worksheet

### Right Triangles

*Solve each triangle described, given the triangle below. Round angle measures to the nearest degree and side measures to the nearest tenth.*

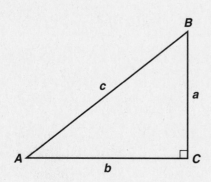

1. $A = 39°12'$, $b = 2.1$

   **$B \approx 51°$, $a \approx 1.7$, $c \approx 2.7$**

2. $a = 9$, $B = 49°$

   **$A \approx 41°$, $b \approx 10.4$, $c \approx 13.7$**

3. $B = 64°$, $b = 19.2$

   **$A \approx 26°$, $a \approx 9.4$, $c \approx 21.4$**

4. $B = 56°48'$, $c = 63.1$

   **$A \approx 33°$, $b \approx 52.8$, $c \approx 34.6$**

5. $A = 16°$, $c = 14$

   **$a \approx 3.9$, $b \approx 13.5$, $B \approx 74°$**

6. $a = 0.4$, $c = 0.5$

   **$A \approx 53°$, $B \approx 37°$, $b \approx 0.3$**

7. $c = 21.3$, $A = 26°20'$

   **$B \approx 64°$, $a \approx 9.4$, $b \approx 19.1$**

8. $a = 2$, $b = 7$

   **$A \approx 16°$, $B \approx 74°$, $c \approx 7.3$**

9. $A = 55°55'$, $c = 16$

   **$B \approx 34°$, $a \approx 13.3$, $b \approx 9.0$**

10. $a = \sqrt{15}$, $B = 18°$

   **$A \approx 72°$, $c \approx 4.1$, $b \approx 1.3$**

Glencoe Division, Macmillan/McGraw-Hill

## 5-6 Practice Worksheet

### The Law of Sines

*Determine the number of possible solutions. If a solution exists, solve the triangle. Round angle measures to the nearest minute and side measures to the nearest tenth.*

**1.** $a = 13.7, A = 25°26', B = 78°$

**2.** $b = 50, a = 33, A = 132°$

**3.** $A = 38°, B = 63°, c = 15$

**4.** $a = 125, A = 25°, b = 150$

**5.** $b = 15.2, A = 12°30', C = 57°30'$

**6.** $a = 32, c = 20, A = 112°$

**7.** $b = 795.1, c = 775.6, B = 51°51'$

**8.** $b = 15, c = 13, C = 50°$

**9.** $a = 12, b = 15, A = 55°$

**10.** $b = 41, A = 33°, B = 29°$

Glencoe Division, Macmillan/McGraw-Hill

## 5-6 Practice Worksheet

### The Law of Sines

*Determine the number of possible solutions. If a solution exists, solve the triangle. Round angle measures to the nearest minute and side measures to the nearest tenth.*

**1.** $a = 13.7, A = 25°26', B = 78°$

    **$b = 31.2, c = 31.0, C=76°34'$**

**2.** $b = 50, a = 33, A = 132°$

    **none**

**3.** $A = 38°, B = 63°, c = 15$

    **$a = 9.4, b = 13.6, C=79°$**

**4.** $a = 125, A = 25°, b = 150$

    **$c = 243.7, B = 30°28', C=124°32'$**

    **$c = 28.2, B = 149°32', C=5°28'$**

**5.** $b = 15.2, A = 12°30', C = 57°30'$

    **$a = 3.5, c = 13.6, B=110°$**

**6.** $a = 32, c = 20, A = 112°$

    **$b = 18.6, B = 32°35', C=35°25'$**

**7.** $b = 795.1, c = 775.6, B = 51°51'$

    **$a = 989.2, A = 78°3', C=50°6'$**

**8.** $b = 15, c = 13, C = 50°$

    **$a = 15.7, A = 67°54', B=62°6'$**

    **$a = 3.6, A = 12°6', B=117°54'$**

**9.** $a = 12, b = 15, A = 55°$

    **none**

**10.** $b = 41, A = 33°, B = 29°$

    **$a = 46.1, c = 74.7, C=118°$**

**Answers may vary due to procedure, rounding, and method of computation.**

Glencoe Division, Macmillan/McGraw-Hill

# Practice Worksheet

## *The Law of Cosines*

*Solve each triangle. Round angle measures to the nearest minute and side measures to the nearest tenth.*

**1.** $a = 1.5, b = 2.3, c = 1.9$        **2.** $b = 40, c = 45, A = 51°$

**3.** $A = 52°, b = 120, c = 160$      **4.** $a = 15, b = 18, c = 17$

**5.** $A = 42°, b = 120, c = 120$      **6.** $a = 15, b = 18, c = 20$

**7.** $b = 12, a = 20, c = 28$        **8.** $a = 12.5, b = 15.1, c = 10.3$

**9.** $c = 49, b = 40, A = 53°$        **10.** $a = 10, c = 8, B = 100°$

## 5-7 | Practice Worksheet

### *The Law of Cosines*

*Solve each triangle. Round angle measures to the nearest minute and side measures to the nearest tenth.*

**1.** $a = 1.5, b = 2.3, c = 1.9$

$A = 40°28', B = 84°16',$
$C=55°16'$

**2.** $b = 40, c = 45, A = 51°$

$a = 36.9, B = 57°24',$
$C=71°36'$

**3.** $A = 52°, b = 120, c = 160$

$a = 127.9, B = 47°41',$
$C=80°19'$

**4.** $a = 15, b = 18, c = 17$

$A = 50°39', B = 68°8',$
$C=61°13'$

**5.** $A = 42°, b = 120, c = 120$

$a = 86.0, B = C=69°0'$

**6.** $a = 15, b = 18, c = 20$

$A = 46°8', B = 59°53',$
$C = 73°59'$

**7.** $b = 12, a = 20, c = 28$

$B = 21°47', A = 38°13',$
$C = 120°0'$

**8.** $a = 12.5, b = 15.1, c = 10.3$

$A = 55°8', B = 82°20',$
$C = 42°32'$

**9.** $c = 49, b = 40, A = 53°$

$a = 40.5, C = 74°58',$
$B = 52°2'$

**10.** $a = 10, c = 8, B = 100°$

$b = 13.8, A = 45°20',$
$C = 34°40'$

## Answers may vary due to procedure, rounding, and method of computation.

Glencoe Division, Macmillan/McGraw-Hill

# 5-8  Practice Worksheet

## *Area of Triangles*

*Find the area of each triangle to the nearest tenth.*

**1.** $c = 3.58, A = 37°40', B = 69°20'$

**2.** $a = 5, b = 12, c = 13$

**3.** $a = 11, b = 13, c = 16$

**4.** $C = 85°, a = 2, B = 19°$

**5.** $A = 50°, b = 12, c = 14$

**6.** $b = 14, C = 110°, B = 25°$

**7.** $b = 15, c = 20, A = 115°$

**8.** $a = 68, c = 110, C = 100°$

*Find the area of each circular segment to the nearest tenth, given its central angle, θ, and the radius of the circle.*

**9.** $\theta = \frac{\pi}{8}, r = 7$

**10.** $\theta = 108°, r = 1.4$

**11.** $\theta = 23°, r = 4.2$

**12.** $\theta = \frac{\pi}{12}, r = 25.25$

Glencoe Division, Macmillan/McGraw-Hill

5-8 **Practice Worksheet**

## Area of Triangles

*Find the area of each triangle to the nearest tenth.*

1. $c = 3.58, A = 37°40', B = 69°20'$
   **3.8 square units**

2. $a = 5, b = 12, c = 13$
   **30 square units**

3. $a = 11, b = 13, c = 16$
   **71.0 square units**

4. $C = 85°, a = 2, B = 19°$
   **0.7 square units**

5. $A = 50°, b = 12, c = 14$
   **64.3 square units**

6. $b = 14, C = 110°, B = 25°$
   **154.1 square units**

7. $b = 15, c = 20, A = 115°$
   **135.9 square units**

8. $a = 68, c = 110, C = 100°$
   **2526.8 square units**

*Find the area of each circular segment to the nearest tenth, given its central angle, $\theta$, and the radius of the circle.*

9. $\theta = \frac{\pi}{8}, r = 7$

   **0.2 square units**

10. $\theta = 108°, r = 1.4$

    **0.9 square units**

11. $\theta = 23°, r = 4.2$

    **0.1 square units**

12. $\theta = \frac{\pi}{12}, r = 25.25$

    **1.0 square units**

Glencoe Division, Macmillan/McGraw-Hill

## 6-1 | Practice Worksheet

## Graphs of the Trigonometric Functions

**Find each value by referring to the graphs of the trigonometric functions.**

**1.** $\sin(-720°)$

**2.** $\tan(-180°)$

**3.** $\cos(540°)$

**4.** $\tan(180°)$

**5.** $\csc(720°)$

**6.** $\sec(180°)$

**Find the values of $\theta$ for which each equation is true.**

**7.** $\sin\theta = -1$

**8.** $\sec\theta = -1$

**9.** $\tan\theta = 0$

**Graph each function on the given interval.**

**10.** $y = \sin x;\ -90° \le x \le 90°$

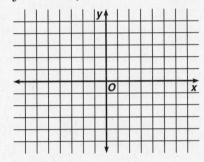

**11.** $y = \tan x;\ -90° \le x \le 270°$

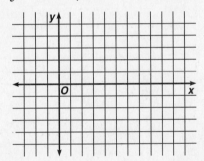

**12.** $y = \cos x;\ -360° \le x \le 360°$

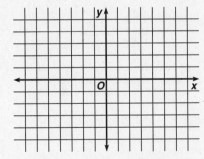

**13.** $y = \sec x;\ -360° \le x \le 360°$

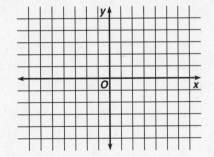

Glencoe Division, Macmillan/McGraw-Hill

**6-1**
# Practice Worksheet

## Graphs of the Trigonometric Functions

*Find each value by referring to the graphs of the trigonometric functions.*

**1.** $\sin(-720°)$
0

**2.** $\tan(-180°)$
0

**3.** $\cos(540°)$
−1

**4.** $\tan(180°)$
0

**5.** $\csc(720°)$
undefined

**6.** $\sec(180°)$
−1

*Find the values of θ for which each equation is true.*

**7.** $\sin \theta = -1$
**270° + 360k°**
**where k is any**
**integer**

**8.** $\sec \theta = -1$
**180° + 360k°**
**where k is any**
**integer**

**9.** $\tan \theta = 0$
**180k°**
**where k is any**
**integer**

*Graph each function on the given interval.*

**10.** $y = \sin x;\ -90° \le x \le 90°$

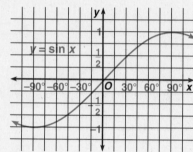

**11.** $y = \tan x;\ -90° \le x \le 270°$

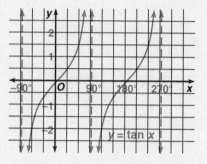

**12.** $y = \cos x;\ -360° \le x \le 360°$

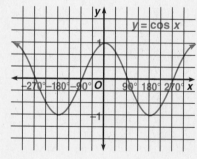

**13.** $y = \sec x;\ -360° \le x \le 360°$

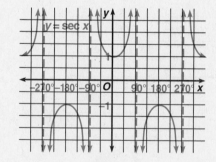

Glencoe Division, Macmillan/McGraw-Hill

## 6-2 Practice Worksheet

## Amplitude, Period, and Phase Shift

*State the amplitude, period, and phase shift for each function.*

**1.** $y = -2 \sin \theta$

**2.** $y = 10 \sec \theta$

**3.** $y = -3 \sin 4\theta$

**4.** $y = 0.5 \sin\left(\theta - \frac{\pi}{3}\right)$

**5.** $y = 2.5 \cos(\theta + 180°)$

**6.** $y = -1.5 \sin\left(4\theta - \frac{\pi}{4}\right)$

*Write an equation of the sine function with each amplitude, period, and phase shift.*

**7.** amplitude = 0.75, period = 360°, phase shift = 30°

**8.** amplitude = 4, period = 3°, phase shift = –30°

*Write an equation of the cosine function with each amplitude, period, and phase shift.*

**9.** amplitude = 3.75, period = 90°, phase shift = 4°

**10.** amplitude = 12, period = 45°, phase shift = 180°

*Graph each function.*

**11.** $y = 0.5 \sin x$

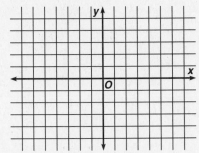

**12.** $y = 2 \cos(3x)$

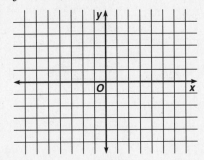

**13.** $y = 2 \cos(2x - 45°)$

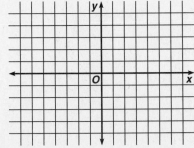

**14.** $y = \tan(x + 60°)$

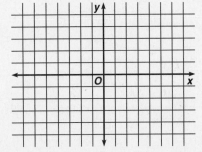

## 6-2 Practice Worksheet

### Amplitude, Period, and Phase Shift

**State the amplitude, period, and phase shift for each function.**

**1.** $y = -2 \sin \theta$

**2, 360°, 0°**

**2.** $y = 10 \sec \theta$

**none, 360°, 0°**

**3.** $y = -3 \sin 4\theta$

**3, 90°, 0°**

**4.** $y = 0.5 \sin \left( \theta - \frac{\pi}{3} \right)$

**0.5, 360°, 60°**

**5.** $y = 2.5 \cos (\theta + 180°)$

**2.5, 360°, −180°**

**6.** $y = -1.5 \sin \left( 4\theta - \frac{\pi}{4} \right)$

**1.5, 90°, 11.25°**

**Write an equation of the sine function with each amplitude, period, and phase shift.**

**7.** amplitude = 0.75, period = 360°, phase shift = 30°

$y = 0.75 \sin (\theta - 30°)$ **or** $y = -0.75 \sin (\theta - 30°)$

**8.** amplitude = 4, period = 3°, phase shift = −30°

$y = \pm 4 \sin (120\theta - 3600°)$

**Write an equation of the cosine function with each amplitude, period, and phase shift.**

**9.** amplitude = 3.75, period = 90°, phase shift = 4°

$y = \pm 3.75 \cos (4\theta - 16°)$

**10.** amplitude = 12, period = 45°, phase shift = 180°

$y = \pm 12 \cos (8\theta - 1440°)$

**Graph each function.**

**11.** $y = 0.5 \sin x$

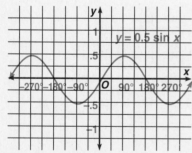

**12.** $y = 2 \cos (3x)$

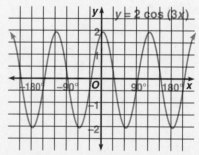

**13.** $y = 2 \cos (2x - 45°)$

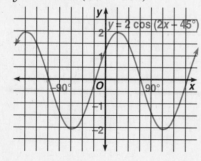

**14.** $y = \tan (x + 60°)$

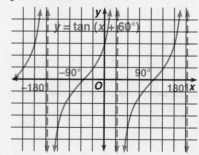

# 6-3 | **Practice Worksheet**

## Graphing Trigonometric Functions

**Graph each function.**

**1.** $y = 2 \sin (x - 45°)$

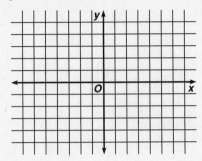

**2.** $y = -2 \cos (3\theta)$

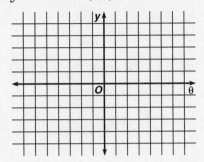

**3.** $y = \frac{1}{2} \cos \left(x - \frac{\pi}{2}\right)$

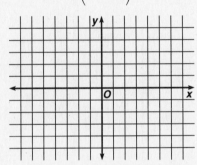

**4.** $y = \sin \left(\frac{x}{2} + 90°\right)$

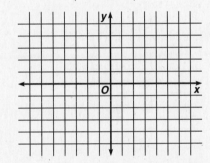

**5.** $y = \sin x + \cos x$

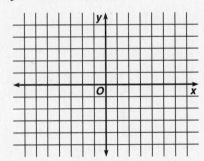

**6.** $y = \cos 2x - \cos x$

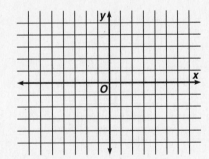

Glencoe Division, Macmillan/McGraw-Hill

**6-3** # Practice Worksheet

## Graphing Trigonometric Functions

*Graph each function.*

**1.** $y = 2 \sin (x - 45°)$

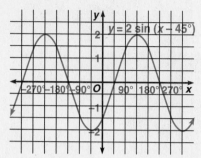

**2.** $y = -2 \cos (3\theta)$

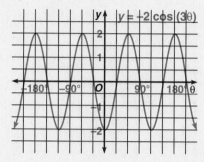

**3.** $y = \frac{1}{2} \cos \left( x - \frac{\pi}{2} \right)$

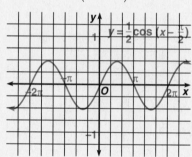

**4.** $y = \sin \left( \frac{x}{2} + 90° \right)$

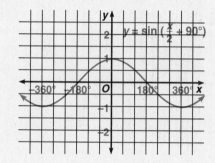

**5.** $y = \sin x + \cos x$

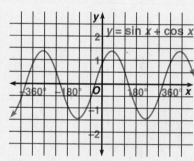

**6.** $y = \cos 2x - \cos x$

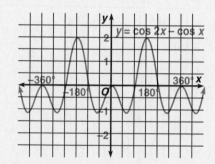

Glencoe Division, Macmillan/McGraw-Hill

## 6-4 Practice Worksheet

## Inverse Trigonometric Functions

**Write each equation in the form of an inverse relation.**

**1.** $0.75 = \sin x$

**2.** $-1 = \cos x$

**3.** $0.1 = \tan \theta$

**4.** $\frac{3}{5} = \cos x$

**5.** $\sin x = \frac{\sqrt{3}}{2}$

**6.** $\cos \alpha = \frac{12}{13}$

**Find the values of x in the interval $0° \leq x \leq 360°$ that satisfy each equation.**

**7.** $x = \arccos 1$

**8.** $\arccos \frac{\sqrt{2}}{2} = x$

**9.** $\arcsin \frac{1}{2} = x$

**10.** $\sin^{-1}(-1) = x$

**11.** $\sin^{-1} \frac{\sqrt{2}}{2} = x$

**12.** $\cot^{-1} 1 = x$

**Evaluate each expression. Assume that all angles are in Quadrant I.**

**13.** $\cos\left(\cos^{-1} \frac{1}{2}\right)$

**14.** $\sin\left(\cos^{-1} \frac{1}{2}\right)$

**15.** $\cos\left(\sin^{-1} \frac{1}{2}\right)$

**16.** $\tan\left(\sin^{-1} \frac{\sqrt{2}}{2} - \cos^{-1} \frac{\sqrt{2}}{2}\right)$

**17.** Verify that $\sin^{-1} \frac{\sqrt{3}}{2} + \sin^{-1} \frac{1}{2} = 90°$. Assume that all angles are in Quadrant I.

Glencoe Division, Macmillan/McGraw-Hill

**6-4**

# Practice Worksheet

## Inverse Trigonometric Functions

**Write each equation in the form of an inverse relation.**

**1.** $0.75 = \sin x$
$x = \text{arcsin } 0.75$

**2.** $-1 = \cos x$
$x = \text{arccos } (-1)$

**3.** $0.1 = \tan \theta$
$\theta = \text{arctan } 0.1$

**4.** $\frac{3}{5} = \cos x$

$x = \text{arccos } \frac{3}{5}$

**5.** $\sin x = \frac{\sqrt{3}}{2}$

$x = \text{arcsin } \frac{\sqrt{3}}{2}$

**6.** $\cos \alpha = \frac{12}{13}$

$\alpha = \text{arccos } \frac{12}{13}$

**Find the values of x in the interval $0° \le x \le 360°$ that satisfy each equation.**

**7.** $x = \arccos 1$

$0°, 360°$

**8.** $\arccos \frac{\sqrt{2}}{2} = x$

$45°, 315°$

**9.** $\arcsin \frac{1}{2} = x$

$3°, 150°$

**10.** $\sin^{-1}(-1) = x$

$270°$

**11.** $\sin^{-1} \frac{\sqrt{2}}{2} = x$

$45°, 135°$

**12.** $\cot^{-1} 1 = x$

$45°, 225°$

**Evaluate each expression. Assume that all angles are in Quadrant I.**

**13.** $\cos\left(\cos^{-1} \frac{1}{2}\right)$

$0.5$

**14.** $\sin\left(\cos^{-1} \frac{1}{2}\right)$

$\frac{\sqrt{3}}{2}$

**15.** $\cos\left(\sin^{-1} \frac{1}{2}\right)$

$\frac{\sqrt{3}}{2}$

**16.** $\tan\left(\sin^{-1} \frac{\sqrt{2}}{2} - \cos^{-1} \frac{\sqrt{2}}{2}\right)$

$0$

**17.** Verify that $\sin^{-1} \frac{\sqrt{3}}{2} + \sin^{-1} \frac{1}{2} = 90°$. Assume that all angles are in Quadrant I.

$\sin^{-1} \frac{\sqrt{3}}{2} + \sin^{-1} \frac{1}{2} = 60° + 30° = 90°$

Glencoe Division, Macmillan/McGraw-Hill

# 6-5 Practice Worksheet

## Principal Values of the Inverse Trigonometric Functions

*Find each value.*

**1.** Arcsin (–1)

**2.** Arccos 1

**3.** Arctan (–1)

**4.** $\text{Cos}^{-1}\frac{1}{2}$

**5.** Arcsin 1

**6.** $\text{Tan}^{-1}\left(-\frac{\sqrt{3}}{3}\right)$

**7.** $\cos\left(\text{Cos}^{-1}\left(-\frac{1}{2}\right)\right)$

**8.** $\sin\left(\text{Sin}^{-1}\frac{\sqrt{3}}{2}\right)$

**9.** $\tan\left(\text{Tan}^{-1}\frac{\sqrt{3}}{3}\right)$

**10.** $\text{Cos}^{-1}\left(\text{Cos}\frac{\pi}{2}\right)$

**11.** $\text{Sin}^{-1}\left(\sin\frac{\pi}{4}\right)$

**12.** $\text{Tan}^{-1}\left(\tan\frac{\pi}{3}\right)$

**13.** $\cos\left(\text{Arcsin}\frac{1}{2}\right)$

**14.** $\sin\left(\text{Arccos}\frac{3}{2}\right)$

**15.** $\tan\left(\text{Arcsin}\frac{\sqrt{3}}{3}\right)$

**16.** $\tan\left(\frac{1}{2}\text{ Arccos}\frac{5}{13}\right)$

**17.** $\cos\left(\frac{1}{2}\text{ Arcsin}\frac{6}{10}\right)$

**18.** $\sin\left(2\text{ Arccos}\frac{3}{5}\right)$

**19.** $\sin\left[\text{Cos}^{-1}\left(\frac{\sqrt{2}}{2}\right)-\frac{\pi}{4}\right]$

**20.** $\cos\left[\text{Sin}^{-1}\left(\frac{\sqrt{2}}{2}\right)+\frac{\pi}{4}\right]$

**21.** $\text{Tan}\left[\frac{3\pi}{4}+\text{Sin}^{-1}\frac{\sqrt{2}}{2}\right]$

# Practice Worksheet

## Principal Values of the Inverse Trigonometric Functions

**Find each value.**

**1.** Arcsin (−1)

**−90°**

**2.** Arccos 1

**0°**

**3.** Arctan (−1)

**−45°**

**4.** $\text{Cos}^{-1} \frac{1}{2}$

**60°**

**5.** Arcsin 1

**90°**

**6.** $\text{Tan}^{-1}\left(-\frac{\sqrt{3}}{3}\right)$

**−30°**

**7.** $\cos\left(\text{Cos}^{-1}\left(-\frac{1}{2}\right)\right)$

$-\dfrac{1}{2}$

**8.** $\sin\left(\text{Sin}^{-1}\frac{\sqrt{3}}{2}\right)$

$\dfrac{\sqrt{3}}{2}$

**9.** $\tan\left(\text{Tan}^{-1}\frac{\sqrt{3}}{3}\right)$

$\dfrac{\sqrt{3}}{3}$

**10.** $\text{Cos}^{-1}\left(\text{Cos}\,\frac{\pi}{2}\right)$

$\dfrac{\pi}{2}$

**11.** $\text{Sin}^{-1}\left(\sin\,\frac{\pi}{4}\right)$

$\dfrac{\pi}{4}$

**12.** $\text{Tan}^{-1}\left(\tan\,\frac{\pi}{3}\right)$

$\dfrac{\pi}{3}$

**13.** $\cos\left(\text{Arcsin}\,\frac{1}{2}\right)$

$\dfrac{\sqrt{3}}{2}$

**14.** $\sin\left(\text{Arccos}\,\frac{3}{2}\right)$

$\dfrac{1}{2}$

**15.** $\tan\left(\text{Arcsin}\,\frac{\sqrt{3}}{3}\right)$

$\dfrac{\sqrt{2}}{2}$

**16.** $\tan\left(\frac{1}{2}\,\text{Arccos}\,\frac{5}{13}\right)$

$\dfrac{2}{3}$

**17.** $\cos\left(\frac{1}{2}\,\text{Arcsin}\,\frac{6}{10}\right)$

$\dfrac{3\sqrt{10}}{10}$

**18.** $\sin\left(2\,\text{Arccos}\,\frac{3}{5}\right)$

$\dfrac{24}{25}$

**19.** $\sin\left[\text{Cos}^{-1}\left(\frac{\sqrt{2}}{2}\right)-\frac{\pi}{4}\right]$

**0**

**20.** $\cos\left[\text{Sin}^{-1}\left(\frac{\sqrt{2}}{2}\right)+\frac{\pi}{4}\right]$

**0**

**21.** $\text{Tan}\left[\frac{3\pi}{4}+\text{Sin}^{-1}\frac{\sqrt{2}}{2}\right]$

**0**

Glencoe Division, Macmillan/McGraw-Hill

## 6-6 Practice Worksheet

## Graphing Inverses of Trigonometric Functions

**State the domain and range of each relation.**

**1.** $y = \mathrm{Sin}\,x + 1$

**2.** $y = \sin x + 1$

**3.** $y = \cos x - 1$

**4.** $y = \mathrm{Cos}^{-1} x$

**5.** $y = \arcsin x$

**6.** $y = \mathrm{Tan}^{-1} x$

**Write the equation for the inverse of each function. Then graph the function and its inverse.**

**7.** $y = \mathrm{Cos}^{-1} x$

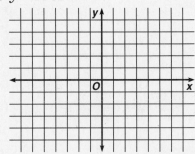

**8.** $y = \mathrm{Tan}^{-1}(3x)$

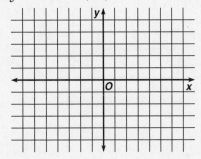

**9.** $y = \frac{\pi}{2} + \mathrm{Cos}^{-1} x$

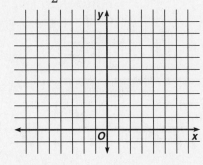

**10.** $y = \mathrm{Sin}\left(x - \frac{\pi}{2}\right)$

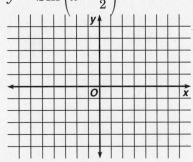

**Determine if each of the following is true or false. If false, give a counterexample.**

**11.** $\mathrm{Cos}^{-1} x = \mathrm{Cos}^{-1}(-x)$

**12.** $\mathrm{Sin}^{-1} x = -\mathrm{Sin}^{-1} x$

## 6-6 Practice Worksheet

### Graphing Inverses of Trigonometric Functions

*State the domain and range of each relation.*

**1.** $y = \operatorname{Sin} x + 1$
domain:
$-90° \leq x \leq 90°$
range: $0 \leq y \leq 2$

**2.** $y = \sin x + 1$
domain:
all real numbers
range: $0 \leq y \leq 2$

**3.** $y = \cos x - 1$
domain:
all real numbers
range: $-2 \leq y \leq 0$

**4.** $y = \operatorname{Cos}^{-1} x$
domain:
$-1 \leq x \leq 1$
range: $0° \leq y \leq 180°$

**5.** $y = \arcsin x$
domain:
$-1 \leq x \leq 1$
range:
all real numbers

**6.** $y = \operatorname{Tan}^{-1} x$
domain:
all real numbers
range:
$-90° \leq y \leq 90°$

*Write the equation for the inverse of each function. Then graph the function and its inverse.*

**7.** $y = \operatorname{Cos}^{-1} x$

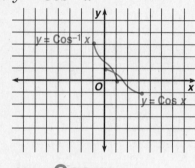

$$y = \operatorname{Cos} x$$

**8.** $y = \operatorname{Tan}^{-1}(3x)$

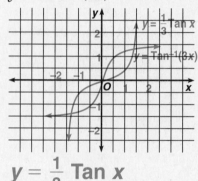

$$y = \frac{1}{3} \operatorname{Tan} x$$

**9.** $y = \frac{\pi}{2} + \operatorname{Cos}^{-1} x$

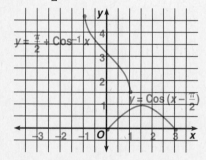

$$y = \operatorname{Cos}\left(x - \frac{\pi}{2}\right)$$

**10.** $y = \operatorname{Sin}\left(x - \frac{\pi}{2}\right)$

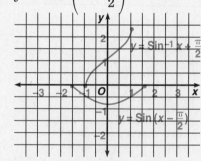

$$y = \operatorname{Sin}^{-1} x + \frac{\pi}{2}$$

*Determine if each of the following is true or false. If false, give a counterexample.*

**11.** $\operatorname{Cos}^{-1} x = \operatorname{Cos}^{-1}(-x)$    false; Let $x = 1$. $\operatorname{Cos}^{-1} = 0°$ but
$\operatorname{Cos}^{-1}(-1) = 180°$.  So, $\operatorname{Cos}^{-1} x \neq \operatorname{Cos}^{-1}(-x)$ for all $x$.

**12.** $\operatorname{Sin}^{-1} x = -\operatorname{Sin}^{-1} x$    false; Let $x = 1$. $\operatorname{Sin}^{-1} 1 = 90°$ but
$-\operatorname{Sin}^{-1} x = -90°$.  So, $\operatorname{Sin}^{-1} x \neq -\operatorname{Sin}^{-1} x$ for all $x$.

Glencoe Division, Macmillan/McGraw-Hill

# 6-7 Practice Worksheet

## Simple Harmonic Motion

**Find the amplitude, period, frequency, and phase shift.**

**1.** $y = 3 \sin\left(\frac{1}{2}\theta - 90°\right)$

**2.** $y = -\frac{1}{2} \cos \theta$

**3.** $y = \sin\left(x + \frac{3\pi}{2}\right)$

**4.** $y = -2 \sin\left(2x - \frac{\pi}{6}\right)$

**5.** $y = 1.5 \cos\left(\frac{\pi}{6}x + \frac{\pi}{3}\right)$

**6.** $y = 12 \cos\left(2\pi t - \frac{\pi}{6}\right)$

**7.** $w = -220 \cos 12t$

**8.** $z = -0.3 \sin\left(\frac{3\pi t}{4} - \frac{\pi}{4}\right)$

*Write an equation with phase shift 0 to represent simple harmonic motion under each set of circumstances.*

**9.** initial position 12, amplitude 12, period 8

**10.** initial position 0, amplitude 2, period $8\pi$

**11.** initial position –24, amplitude 24, period 6

Glencoe Division, Macmillan/McGraw-Hill

## 6-7 | Practice Worksheet

### Simple Harmonic Motion

**Find the amplitude, period, frequency, and phase shift.**

**1.** $y = 3 \sin \left( \frac{1}{2}\theta - 90° \right)$

$$3, 720°, \frac{1}{720}, 180°$$

**2.** $y = -\frac{1}{2} \cos \theta$

$$\frac{1}{2}, 360°, \frac{1}{360}, 0°$$

**3.** $y = \sin \left( x + \frac{3\pi}{2} \right)$

$$1, 2\pi, \frac{1}{2\pi}, -\frac{3\pi}{2}$$

**4.** $y = -2 \sin \left( 2x - \frac{\pi}{6} \right)$

$$2, \pi, \frac{1}{\pi}, \frac{\pi}{12}$$

**5.** $y = 1.5 \cos \left( \frac{\pi}{6} x + \frac{\pi}{3} \right)$

$$1.5, 12, \frac{1}{12}, -2$$

**6.** $y = 12 \cos \left( 2\pi t - \frac{\pi}{6} \right)$

$$12, 1, 1, \frac{1}{12}$$

**7.** $w = -220 \cos 12t$

$$220, 30°, \frac{1}{30}, 0°$$

**8.** $z = -0.3 \sin \left( \frac{3\pi t}{4} - \frac{\pi}{4} \right)$

$$0.3, \frac{8}{3}, \frac{3}{8}, \frac{1}{3}$$

**Write an equation with phase shift 0 to represent simple harmonic motion under each set of circumstances.**

**9.** initial position 12, amplitude 12, period 8

$$y = 12 \cos \frac{\pi t}{4}$$

**10.** initial position 0, amplitude 2, period $8\pi$

$$y = \pm 2 \sin \frac{t}{4}$$

**11.** initial position –24, amplitude 24, period 6

$$y = -24 \cos \frac{\pi t}{3}$$

Glencoe Division, Macmillan/McGraw-Hill

# 7-1 Practice Worksheet

## Basic Trigonometric Identities

**Solve for values of θ between 0° and 90°.**

**1.** If $\tan \theta = 2$, find $\cot \theta$ .

**2.** If $\sin \theta = \frac{2}{3}$, find $\cos \theta$.

**3.** If $\cos \theta = \frac{1}{4}$ , find $\tan \theta$

**4.** If $\tan \theta = 3$, find $\sec \theta$.

**5.** If $\sin \theta = \frac{7}{10}$, find $\cot \theta$ .

**6.** If $\tan \theta = \frac{7}{2}$, find $\sin \theta$ .

**Express each value as a function of an angle in Quadrant I.**

**7.** $\sin 458°$

**8.** $\cos 892°$

**9.** $\tan (-876°)$

**10.** $\csc 495°$

**Simplify.**

**11.** $\dfrac{\cot A}{\tan A}$

**12.** $\dfrac{\sin^2 \beta \cot \beta}{\cos \beta}$

**13.** $\sin^2 \theta \cos^2 \theta - \cos^2 \theta$

**14.** $\cos x + \sin x \tan x$

# 7-1 Practice Worksheet

## Basic Trigonometric Identities

*Solve for values of θ between 0° and 90°.*

**1.** If $\tan \theta = 2$, find $\cot \theta$.

$$\frac{1}{2}$$

**2.** If $\sin \theta = \frac{2}{3}$, find $\cos \theta$.

$$\frac{\sqrt{5}}{3}$$

**3.** If $\cos \theta = \frac{1}{4}$, find $\tan \theta$

$$\sqrt{15}$$

**4.** If $\tan \theta = 3$, find $\sec \theta$.

$$\sqrt{10}$$

**5.** If $\sin \theta = \frac{7}{10}$, find $\cot \theta$.

$$\frac{51}{7}$$

**6.** If $\tan \theta = \frac{7}{2}$, find $\sin \theta$.

$$\frac{7\sqrt{53}}{53}$$

**Express each value as a function of an angle in Quadrant I.**

**7.** $\sin 458°$
$\sin 82°$

**8.** $\cos 892°$
$-\cos 8°$

**9.** $\tan(-876°)$
$\tan 24°$

**10.** $\csc 495°$
$\csc 45°$

**Simplify.**

**11.** $\dfrac{\cot A}{\tan A}$

$\cot^2 A$

**12.** $\dfrac{\sin^2 \beta \cot \beta}{\cos \beta}$

$\sin \beta$

**13.** $\sin^2 \theta \cos^2 \theta - \cos^2 \theta$
$-\cos^4 \theta$

**14.** $\cos x + \sin x \tan x$
$\sec x$

Glencoe Division, Macmillan/McGraw-Hill

## 7-2 Practice Worksheet

## Verifying Trigonometric Identities

**Verify that each of the following is an identity.**

1. $\dfrac{\csc x}{\cot x + \tan x} = \cos x$

2. $\sin^3 x - \cos^3 x = (1 + \sin x \cos x)(\sin x - \cos x)$

3. $\dfrac{1}{\sin y - 1} - \dfrac{1}{\sin y + 1} = -2\sec^2 y$

4. $1 - 2\sin^2 r + \sin^4 r = \cos^4 r$

5. $\tan u + \dfrac{\cos u}{1 + \sin u} = \sec u$

6. $\dfrac{\tan x + \sec x}{\sec x - \cos x + \tan x} = \csc x$

**Find a numerical value of one trigonometric function of each x.**

7. $\sin x = 3 \cos x$

8. $\cos x = \cot x$

## 7-2 Practice Worksheet

## Verifying Trigonometric Identities

**Verify that each of the following is an identity.**

**1.** $\dfrac{\csc x}{\cot x + \tan x} = \cos x$

$$\dfrac{\csc x}{\cot x + \tan x} = \dfrac{\dfrac{1}{\sin x}}{\dfrac{\cos x}{\sin x} + \dfrac{\sin x}{\cos x}} \cdot \dfrac{\sin x \cos x}{\sin x \cos x} = \dfrac{\cos x}{\cos^2 x \sin^2 x}$$

$$= \dfrac{\cos x}{1} = \cos x$$

**2.** $\sin^3 x - \cos^3 x = (1 + \sin x \cos x)(\sin x - \cos x)$

$$\sin^3 x - \cos^3 x = (\sin x - \cos x)(\sin^2 x + \sin x \cos x + \cos^2 x)$$
$$= (\sin x - \cos x)(1 + \sin x \cos x)$$

**3.** $\dfrac{1}{\sin y - 1} - \dfrac{1}{\sin y + 1} = -2\sec^2 y$

$$\dfrac{1}{\sin y - 1} - \dfrac{1}{\sin y + 1} = \dfrac{\sin y + 1 - \sin y + 1}{\sin^2 y - 1} = \dfrac{2}{-\cos^2 y} = -2\sec^2 y$$

**4.** $1 - 2\sin^2 r + \sin^4 r = \cos^4 r$

$$\cos^4 r = (1 - \sin^2 r)^2 = 1 - 2\sin^2 r + \sin^4 r$$

**5.** $\tan u + \dfrac{\cos u}{1 + \sin u} = \sec u$

$$\tan u + \dfrac{\cos u}{1 + \sin u} = \dfrac{\sin u}{\cos u} + \dfrac{\cos u}{1 + \sin u} = \dfrac{\sin u + \sin^2 u + \cos^2 u}{(\cos u)(1 + \sin u)}$$

$$= \dfrac{1 + \sin u}{(\cos u)(1 + \sin u)} = \sec u$$

**6.** $\dfrac{\tan x + \sec x}{\sec x - \cos x + \tan x} = \csc x$

$$\dfrac{\sin x + 1}{1 - \cos^2 x + \sin x} = \dfrac{\sin x + 1}{\sin^2 x + \sin x} = \dfrac{\sin x + 1}{(\sin x)(\sin x + 1)} = \csc x$$

**Find a numerical value of one trigonometric function of each x.**

**7.** $\sin x = 3\cos x$
$$\tan x = 3$$

**8.** $\cos x = \cot x$
$$\csc x = 1 \text{ or } \sin x = 1$$

Glencoe Division, Macmillan/McGraw-Hill

# 7-3 Practice Worksheet

## Sum and Difference Identities

**Use the sum and difference identities to find the exact value of each function.**

**1.** $\cos 75°$

**2.** $\cos 375°$

**3.** $\sin(-165°)$

**4.** $\sin(-105°)$

**5.** $\sin 95° \cos 55° + \cos 95° \sin 55°$

**6.** $\cos 160° \cos 40° + \sin 160° \sin 40°$

**7.** $\tan(135° + 120°)$

**8.** $\tan 345°$

**If $\alpha$ and $\beta$ are the measures of two first quadrant angles, find the exact value of each function.**

**9.** If $\sin \alpha = \frac{12}{13}$ and $\cos \beta = \frac{3}{5}$, find $\cos(\alpha - \beta)$.

**10.** If $\cos \alpha = \frac{12}{13}$ and $\cos \beta = \frac{12}{37}$, find $\tan(\alpha - \beta)$.

**11.** If $\cos \alpha = \frac{8}{17}$ and $\tan \beta = \frac{5}{12}$, find $\cos(\alpha + \beta)$.

**12.** If $\csc \alpha = \frac{13}{12}$ and $\sec \beta = \frac{5}{3}$, find $\sin(\alpha - \beta)$.

**Verify that each of the following is an identity.**

**13.** $\cos(180° - \theta) = -\cos \theta$

**14.** $\sin(360° + \theta) = \sin \theta$

Glencoe Division, Macmillan/McGraw-Hill

**7-3**

# Practice Worksheet

## Sum and Difference Identities

*Use the sum and difference identities to find the exact value of each function.*

**1.** cos 75°

$$\frac{\sqrt{6} - \sqrt{2}}{4}$$

**2.** cos 375°

$$\frac{\sqrt{6} + \sqrt{2}}{4}$$

**3.** sin (−165°)

$$\frac{\sqrt{2} - \sqrt{6}}{4}$$

**4.** sin (−105°)

$$\frac{-\sqrt{2} - \sqrt{6}}{4}$$

**5.** sin 95° cos 55° + cos 95° sin 55°

$$\frac{1}{2}$$

**6.** cos 160° cos 40° + sin 160° sin 40°

$$-\frac{1}{2}$$

**7.** tan (135° + 120°)

$$2 + \sqrt{3}$$

**8.** tan 345°

$$\sqrt{3} - 2$$

*If α and β are the measures of two first quadrant angles, find the exact value of each function.*

**9.** If $\sin \alpha = \frac{12}{13}$ and $\cos \beta = \frac{3}{5}$, find cos (α − β).   $\frac{63}{65}$

**10.** If $\cos \alpha = \frac{12}{13}$ and $\cos \beta = \frac{12}{37}$, find tan (α − β ).   $-\frac{360}{319}$

**11.** If $\cos \alpha = \frac{8}{17}$ and $\tan \beta = \frac{5}{12}$, find cos (α + β).   $\frac{21}{221}$

**12.** If $\csc \alpha = \frac{13}{12}$ and $\sec \beta = \frac{5}{3}$, find sin (α − β).   $\frac{16}{65}$

*Verify that each of the following is an identity.*

**13.** cos (180° − θ) = − cos θ

$$\cos (180° - θ)$$
$$= \cos 180° \cos θ + \sin 180° \sin θ$$
$$= (-1) \cos θ + 0 \cdot \sin θ$$
$$= - \cos θ$$

**14.** sin (360° + θ) = sin θ

$$\sin (360° + θ)$$
$$= \sin 360° \cos θ + \cos 360° \sin θ$$
$$= 0 \cdot \cos θ + 1 \cdot \sin θ$$
$$= \sin θ$$

Glencoe Division, Macmillan/McGraw-Hill

# 7-4 Practice Worksheet

## Double-Angle and Half-Angle Identities

If $\sin A = \frac{12}{13}$ and A is in the first quadrant, find each value.

**1.** $\cos 2A$

**2.** $\sin 2A$

**3.** $\tan 2A$

**4.** $\cos \frac{A}{2}$

**5.** $\sin \frac{A}{2}$

**6.** $\tan \frac{A}{2}$

### Use a half-angle identity to find each value.

**7.** $\tan \frac{\pi}{8}$

**8.** $\cos \frac{5\pi}{8}$

**9.** $\sin \frac{19\pi}{12}$

**10.** $\cos 67\frac{1}{2}°$

### Verify that each of the following is an identity.

**11.** $\tan \frac{A}{2} = \frac{\sin A}{1 + \cos A}$

**12.** $\tan \frac{A}{2} = \frac{1 - \cos A}{\sin A}$

Glencoe Division, Macmillan/McGraw-Hill

## 7-4 Practice Worksheet

## Double-Angle and Half-Angle Identities

If $\sin A = \frac{12}{13}$ and A is in the first quadrant, find each value.

**1.** $\cos 2A$

$-\dfrac{119}{169}$

**2.** $\sin 2A$

$\dfrac{120}{169}$

**3.** $\tan 2A$

$-\dfrac{120}{119}$

**4.** $\cos \dfrac{A}{2}$

$\dfrac{3\sqrt{13}}{13}$

**5.** $\sin \dfrac{A}{2}$

$\dfrac{2\sqrt{13}}{13}$

**6.** $\tan \dfrac{A}{2}$

$\dfrac{2}{3}$

**Use a half-angle identity to find each value.**

**7.** $\tan \dfrac{\pi}{8}$

$\sqrt{\dfrac{2-\sqrt{2}}{2+\sqrt{2}}}$

**8.** $\cos \dfrac{5\pi}{8}$

$\dfrac{\sqrt{2}}{2}$

**9.** $\sin \dfrac{19\pi}{12}$

$-\dfrac{\sqrt{2+\sqrt{3}}}{2}$

**10.** $\cos 67\frac{1}{2}°$

$\dfrac{\sqrt{2-\sqrt{2}}}{2}$

**Verify that each of the following is an identity.**

**11.** $\tan \dfrac{A}{2} = \dfrac{\sin A}{1+\cos A}$

$$\tan \dfrac{A}{2} = \sqrt{\dfrac{1-\cos A}{1+\cos A}} \cdot \sqrt{\dfrac{1+\cos A}{1+\cos A}}$$

$$= \sqrt{\dfrac{1-\cos^2 A}{(1+\cos A)^2}}$$

$$= \dfrac{\sin A}{1+\cos A}$$

**12.** $\tan \dfrac{A}{2} = \dfrac{1-\cos A}{\sin A}$

$$\tan \dfrac{A}{2} = \dfrac{\sin A}{1+\cos A} \cdot \dfrac{1-\cos A}{1-\cos A}$$

$$= \dfrac{\sin A\,(1-\cos A)}{1-\cos^2 A}$$

$$= \dfrac{\sin A\,(1-\cos A)}{\sin^2 A} = \dfrac{1-\cos}{\sin}$$

Glencoe Division, Macmillan/McGraw-Hill

**7-5** **Practice Worksheet**

## Solving Trigonometric Equations

***Solve each equation for all values of x.***

1. $2 \sin^2 x - 5 \sin x + 2 = 0$

2. $\sin^2 x - 2 \sin x - 3 = 0$

3. $3 \cos 2x - 5 \cos x = 1$

4. $2 \tan x \cos x + 2 \cos x = \tan x + 1$

***Solve each equation for $0° \le x \le 180°$.***

5. $2 \sin^2 x - 1 = 0$

6. $\cos x = 3 \cos x - 2$

7. $\tan x = \sin x$

8. $\cos x \sin 2x = 0$

9. $\sec x = 1 + \tan x$

10. $4 \sin^2 x - 4 \sin x + 1 = 0$

11. $\sin 2x = 2 \cos x$

12. $\tan^2 x + \tan x = 0$

13. $2 \sin 2x = 1$

14. $\cos 2x + \sin x = 1$

Glencoe Division, Macmillan/McGraw-Hill

7-5

# Practice Worksheet

## Solving Trigonometric Equations

**Solve each equation for all values of x.**

1. $2 \sin^2 x - 5 \sin x + 2 = 0$
   $30° + 360k°, 150° + 360k°$

2. $\sin^2 x - 2 \sin x - 3 = 0$
   $270° + 360k°$

3. $3 \cos 2x - 5 \cos x = 1$
   $120° + 360k°, 240° + 360k°$

4. $2 \tan x \cos x + 2 \cos x = \tan x + 1$
   $-60 + 360k°, -45° + 180k°$
   $60° + 360k°$

**Solve each equation for $0° \le x \le 180°$.**

5. $2 \sin^2 x - 1 = 0$
   $45°, 135°$

6. $\cos x = 3 \cos x - 2$
   $0°$

7. $\tan x = \sin x$
   $0°, 180°$

8. $\cos x \sin 2x = 0$
   $0°, 90°, 180°$

9. $\sec x = 1 + \tan x$
   $0°$

10. $4 \sin^2 x - 4 \sin x + 1 = 0$
    $30°, 150°$

11. $\sin 2x = 2 \cos x$
    $90°$

12. $\tan^2 x + \tan x = 0$
    $0°, 135°, 180°$

13. $2 \sin 2x = 1$
    $15°, 75°$

14. $\cos 2x + \sin x = 1$
    $0°, 30°, 150°, 180°$

Glencoe Division, Macmillan/McGraw-Hill

## 7-6 Practice Worksheet

## *Normal Form of a Linear Equation*

*Write the standard form of the equation of each line given p, the measure of its normal, and $\phi$, the angle the normal makes with the positive x-axis.*

**1.** $p = 4, \ \phi = 30°$

**2.** $p = 2, \ \phi = 45°$

**3.** $p = 3, \ \phi = 60°$

**4.** $p = 12, \ \phi = 120°$

**5.** $p = 8, \ \phi = 150°$

**6.** $p = 15, \ \phi = 225°$

*Write each equation in normal form. Then find the measure of the normal, p, and $\phi$, the angle that the normal makes with the positive x-axis.*

**7.** $3x - 2y - 1 = 0$

**8.** $5x + y - 12 = 0$

**9.** $y = x + 5$

**10.** $y = x - 2$

**11.** $x + y - 5 = 0$

**12.** $2x + y - 1 = 0$

Glencoe Division, Macmillan/McGraw-Hill

## 7-6   Practice Worksheet

## Normal Form of a Linear Equation

*Write the standard form of the equation of each line given p, the measure of its normal, and φ, the angle the normal makes with the positive x-axis.*

**1.** $p = 4,\ \phi = 30°$

$$3x = \sqrt{3}\,y - 8\sqrt{3} = 0$$

**2.** $p = 2,\ \phi = 45°$

$$x + y - 2\sqrt{2} = 0$$

**3.** $p = 3,\ \phi = 60°$

$$x + \sqrt{3}\,y - 6 = 0$$

**4.** $p = 12,\ \phi = 120°$

$$x - \sqrt{3}\,y + 24 = 0$$

**5.** $p = 8,\ \phi = 150°$

$$3x - \sqrt{3}\,y + 16\sqrt{3} = 0$$

**6.** $p = 15,\ \phi = 225°$

$$x + y + 15\sqrt{2} = 0$$

*Write each equation in normal form. Then find the measure of the normal, p, and φ, the angle that the normal makes with the positive x-axis.*

**7.** $3x - 2y - 1 = 0$

$$\frac{3x}{\sqrt{13}} - \frac{2y}{\sqrt{13}} - \frac{1}{\sqrt{13}} = 0;$$

$$326°;\ \frac{1}{\sqrt{13}} \approx 0.28 \text{ units}$$

**8.** $5x + y - 12 = 0$

$$\frac{5x}{\sqrt{26}} + \frac{y}{\sqrt{26}} - \frac{12}{\sqrt{26}} = 0;$$

$$11°;\ \frac{12}{\sqrt{26}} \approx 2.35 \text{ units}$$

**9.** $y = x + 5$

$$-\frac{x}{\sqrt{2}} + \frac{y}{\sqrt{2}} - \frac{5}{\sqrt{2}} = 0;$$

$$\phi = 135°;\ \frac{5}{\sqrt{2}} \approx 3.54 \text{ units}$$

**10.** $y = x - 2$

$$\frac{x}{\sqrt{2}} - \frac{y}{\sqrt{2}} - \frac{2}{\sqrt{2}} = 0;$$

$$\phi = 315°;\ \frac{2}{\sqrt{2}} \approx 1.41 \text{ units}$$

**11.** $x + y - 5 = 0$

$$\frac{x}{\sqrt{2}} + \frac{y}{\sqrt{2}} - \frac{5}{\sqrt{2}} = 0;$$

$$\phi = 45°;\ \frac{5}{\sqrt{2}} \approx 3.54 \text{ units}$$

**12.** $2x + y - 1 = 0$

$$\frac{x}{\sqrt{5}} - \frac{y}{\sqrt{5}} - \frac{1}{\sqrt{5}} = 0;$$

$$\phi = 27°;\ \frac{1}{\sqrt{5}} \approx 0.45 \text{ unit}$$

Glencoe Division, Macmillan/McGraw-Hill

## 7-7 Practice Worksheet

## *Distance from a Point to a LIne*

*Find the distance between the point with the given coordinates and the line with the given equation. Round to the nearest tenth.*

**1.** $(-1, 5), 3x - 4y - 1 = 0$

**2.** $(2, 5), 5x - 12y + 1 = 0$

**3.** $(1, -4), 12x + 5y - 3 = 0$

**4.** $(-1, -3), 6x + 8y - 3 = 0$

*Name the coordinates of one point that satisfy the first equation. Then find the distance from the point to the graph of the second equation.*

**5.** $2x - 3y + 4 = 0$

$\quad y = \dfrac{2}{3} x + 5$

**6.** $4x - y + 1 = 0$

$\quad 4x - y - 8 = 0$

**7.** $x + 3y - 4 = 0$

$\quad x + 3y + 20 = 0$

**8.** $3x - 2y = 6$

$\quad 3x - 2y + 30 = 0$

*Find an equation of the line that bisects the acute angle formed by the graphs of each pair of equations.*

**9.** $x + 2y - 3 = 0$

$\quad x - y + 4 = 0$

**10.** $x + y - 6 = 0$

$\quad x - 2y - 2 = 0$

**11.** $x + y - 5 = 0$

$\quad 2x - y + 7 = 0$

**12.** $2x + y - 3 = 0$

$\quad x - y + 5 = 0$

Glencoe Division, Macmillan/McGraw-Hill

## 7-7 Practice Worksheet

### Distance from a Point to a LIne

Find the distance between the point with the given coordinates and the line with the given equation. Round to the nearest tenth.

**1.** $(-1, 5)$, $3x - 4y - 1 = 0$

4.8

**2.** $(2, 5)$, $5x - 12y + 1 = 0$

$\dfrac{49}{13} \approx 3.77$

**3.** $(1, -4)$, $12x + 5y - 3 = 0$

$\dfrac{11}{13} \approx 0.85$

**4.** $(-1, -3)$, $6x + 8y - 3 = 0$

3.3

Name the coordinates of one point that satisfy the first equation. Then find the distance from the point to the graph of the second equation.

**5.** $2x - 3y + 4 = 0$

$y = \dfrac{2}{3}x + 5$

$\left(0, \dfrac{4}{3}\right)$; $\dfrac{11\sqrt{13}}{13} \approx 3.05$

**6.** $4x - y + 1 = 0$

$4x - y - 8 = 0$

$(0, 1)$; $\dfrac{9}{17} \approx 0.53$

**7.** $x + 3y - 4 = 0$

$x + 3y + 20 = 0$

$\left(0, \dfrac{4}{3}\right)$; $\dfrac{12\sqrt{10}}{5} \approx 7.59$

**8.** $3x - 2y = 6$

$3x - 2y + 30 = 0$

$(0, -3)$; $\dfrac{36\sqrt{13}}{13} \approx 9.98$

Find an equation of the line that bisects the acute angle formed by the graphs of each pair of equations.

**9.** $x + 2y - 3 = 0$

$x - y + 4 = 0$

$(\sqrt{2} - \sqrt{5})x + (2\sqrt{2} + \sqrt{5})y - (3\sqrt{2} + 4\sqrt{5}) = 0$

**10.** $x + y - 6 = 0$

$x - 2y - 2 = 0$

$(\sqrt{2} - \sqrt{5})x - (2\sqrt{2} + \sqrt{5})y - 2\sqrt{2} + 6\sqrt{5} = 0$

**11.** $x + y - 5 = 0$

$2x - y + 7 = 0$

$(\sqrt{5} + 2\sqrt{2})x + (\sqrt{5} - \sqrt{2})y - 5\sqrt{5} + 7\sqrt{2} = 0$

**12.** $2x + y - 3 = 0$

$x - y + 5 = 0$

$(2\sqrt{2} - \sqrt{5})x + (\sqrt{2} + \sqrt{5})y - (3\sqrt{2} + 5\sqrt{5}) = 0$

Glencoe Division, Macmillan/McGraw-Hill

# Practice Worksheet

## *Geometric Vectors*

*Use a metric ruler and a protractor to find each sum or difference. Then, find the magnitude and amplitude of each resultant.*

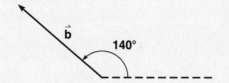

**1. $\vec{a} + \vec{b}$**

**2. $\vec{b} - \vec{c}$**

**3. $2\vec{a} + \vec{b}$**

**4. $\vec{b} + 3\vec{c}$**

*Find the magnitude of the vertical and horizontal components of each vector shown for Exercises 1-4.*

**5. $\vec{a}$**

**6. $\vec{b}$**

**7. $\vec{c}$**

Glencoe Division, Macmillan/McGraw-Hill

## 8-1 | Practice Worksheet

## *Geometric Vectors*

*Use a metric ruler and a protractor to find each sum or difference. Then, find the magnitude and amplitude of each resultant.*

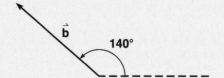

**1.** $\vec{a} + \vec{b}$
39 mm; 110°

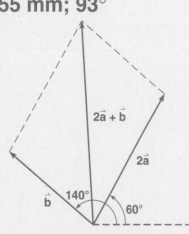

**2.** $\vec{b} - \vec{c}$
40 mm; 139°

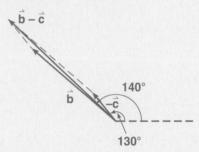

**3.** $2\vec{a} + \vec{b}$
55 mm; 93°

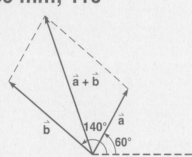

**4.** $\vec{b} + 3\vec{c}$
6 mm; 217°

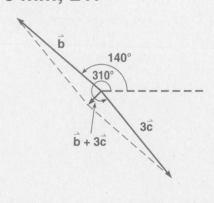

*Find the magnitude of the vertical and horizontal components of each vector shown for Exercises 1-4.*

**5.** $\vec{a}$
$x = 10$ mm
$y \approx 17.3$ mm

**6.** $\vec{b}$
$x \approx -23.0$ mm
$y \approx 19.3$ mm

**7.** $\vec{c}$
$x \approx 6.4$ mm
$y \approx -7.7$ mm

Glencoe Division, Macmillan/McGraw-Hill

NAME _____ DATE _____

# Practice Worksheet

## Algebraic Vectors

**Find the ordered pair that represents the vector from A to B. Then find the magnitude of $\vec{AB}$.**

**1.** $A(2, 4), B(-1, 3)$        **2.** $A(4, -2), B(5, -5)$        **3.** $A(-3, -6), B(8, -1)$

**Find the sum or difference of the given vectors algebraically. Express the result as an ordered pair.**

**4.** $2\vec{i} + 6\vec{j}$                     **5.** $4\vec{i} - 5\vec{j}$

**Find an ordered pair to represent $\vec{u}$ in each equation if $\vec{v} = (2, -1)$ and $\vec{w} = (-3, 5)$.**

**6.** $\vec{u} = \vec{v} + \vec{w}$                **7.** $\vec{u} = \vec{v} - \vec{w}$

**8.** $\vec{u} = 3\vec{v}$                  **9.** $\vec{u} = \vec{w} - 2\vec{v}$

**10.** $\vec{u} = 2\vec{v} + 3\vec{w}$          **11.** $\vec{u} = 5\vec{w} - 2\vec{v}$

Glencoe Division, Macmillan/McGraw-Hill

# 8-2 Practice Worksheet

## Algebraic Vectors

**Find the ordered pair that represents the vector from A to B. Then find the magnitude of $\vec{AB}$.**

**1.** $A(2, 4), B(-1, 3)$
$(-3, -1);\ \sqrt{10}$

**2.** $A(4, -2), B(5, -5)$
$(1, -3);\ \sqrt{10}$

**3.** $A(-3, -6), B(8, -1)$
$(11, 5);\ \sqrt{146}$

**Find the sum or difference of the given vectors algebraically. Express the result as an ordered pair.**

**4.** $2\vec{i} + 6\vec{j}$
$(2, 6)$

**5.** $4\vec{i} - 5\vec{j}$
$(4, -5)$

**Find an ordered pair to represent $\vec{u}$ in each equation if $\vec{v} = (2, -1)$ and $\vec{w} = (-3, 5)$.**

**6.** $\vec{u} = \vec{v} + \vec{w}$
$(-1, 4)$

**7.** $\vec{u} = \vec{v} - \vec{w}$
$(5, -6)$

**8.** $\vec{u} = 3\vec{v}$
$(6, -3)$

**9.** $\vec{u} = \vec{w} - 2\vec{v}$
$(-7, 7)$

**10.** $\vec{u} = 2\vec{v} + 3\vec{w}$
$(-5, 13)$

**11.** $\vec{u} = 5\vec{w} - 2\vec{v}$
$(-19, 27)$

Glencoe Division, Macmillan/McGraw-Hill

**8-3**

# Practice Worksheet

## Vectors in Three-Dimensional Space

*Locate points with the given coordinates. Then find the magnitude of a vector from the origin to each point.*

**1.** $(4, 7, 5)$

**2.** $(3, -2, 6)$

*For each pair of points A and B, find an ordered triple that represents $\overrightarrow{AB}$. Then find the magnitude of $\overrightarrow{AB}$.*

**3.** $A(2, 1, 3), B(-4, 5, 7)$

**4.** $A(4, 0, 6), B(7, 1, -3)$

**5.** $A(-4, 5, 8), B(7, 2, -9)$

**6.** $A(6, 8, -5), B(7, -3, 12)$

*Write each vector as the sum of unit vectors.*

**7.** $(8, -9, 2)$

**8.** $(7, 6, -5)$

*Find an ordered triple to represent $\vec{u}$ in each equation if $\vec{v} = (2, -4, 5)$ and $\vec{w} = (6, -8, 9)$.*

**9.** $\vec{u} = \vec{v} + \vec{w}$

**10.** $\vec{u} = \vec{v} - \vec{w}$

**11.** $\vec{u} = 4\vec{v} + 3\vec{w}$

**12.** $\vec{u} = 5\vec{v} - 2\vec{w}$

Glencoe Division, Macmillan/McGraw-Hill

8-3  # Practice Worksheet

## Vectors in Three-Dimensional Space

*Locate points with the given coordinates. Then find the magnitude of a vector from the origin to each point.*

**1.** $(4, 7, 5)$

$3\sqrt{10}$

**2.** $(3, -2, 6)$

$7$

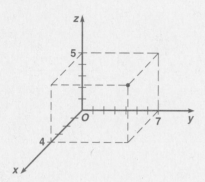

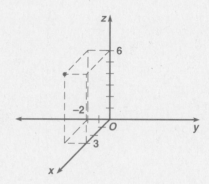

*For each pair of points A and B, find an ordered triple that represents $\overrightarrow{AB}$. Then find the magnitude of $\overrightarrow{AB}$.*

**3.** $A(2, 1, 3), B(-4, 5, 7)$

$(-6, 4, 4); 2\sqrt{17}$

**4.** $A(4, 0, 6), B(7, 1, -3)$

$(3, 1, -9); \sqrt{91}$

**5.** $A(-4, 5, 8), B(7, 2, -9)$

$(11, -3, -17); \sqrt{419}$

**6.** $A(6, 8, -5), B(7, -3, 12)$

$(1, -11, 17); \sqrt{411}$

*Write each vector as the sum of unit vectors.*

**7.** $(8, -9, 2)$

$8\vec{i} - 9\vec{j} + 2\vec{k}$

**8.** $(7, 6, -5)$

$7\vec{i} + 6\vec{j} - 5\vec{k}$

*Find an ordered triple to represent $\vec{u}$ in each equation if $\vec{v} = (2, -4, 5)$ and $\vec{w} = (6, -8, 9)$.*

**9.** $\vec{u} = \vec{v} + \vec{w}$

$(8, -12, 14)$

**10.** $\vec{u} = \vec{v} - \vec{w}$

$(-4, 4, -4)$

**11.** $\vec{u} = 4\vec{v} + 3\vec{w}$

$(26, -40, 47)$

**12.** $\vec{u} = 5\vec{v} - 2\vec{w}$

$(-2, -4, 7)$

Glencoe Division, Macmillan/McGraw-Hill

# 8-4 Practice Worksheet

## Perpendicular Vectors

*Find each inner product and state whether the vectors are perpendicular. Write yes or no.*

**1.** $(3, 6) \cdot (-4, 2)$

**2.** $(-1, 4) \cdot (3, -2)$

**3.** $(2, 0) \cdot (-1, -1)$

**4.** $(7, -3) \cdot (-2, 4)$

**5.** $(-3, 0) \cdot (4, -3)$

**6.** $(7, -4) \cdot (-5, -8)$

**7.** $(-2, 0, 1) \cdot (3, 2, -3)$

**8.** $(-4, -1, 1) \cdot (1, -3, 4)$

**9.** $(0, 0, 1) \cdot (1, -2, 0)$

*Find each cross product. Then verify that the resulting vector is perpendicular to the given vectors.*

**10.** $(1, 3, 4) \times (-1, 0, -1)$

**11.** $(3, 1, -6) \times (-2, 4, 3)$

**12.** $(3, 1, 2) \times (2, -3, 1)$

**13.** $(4, -1, 0) \times (5, -3, -1)$

**14.** $(-6, 1, 3) \times (-2, -2, 1)$

**15.** $(0, 0, 6) \times (3, -2, -4)$

Glencoe Division, Macmillan/McGraw-Hill

## 8-4 Practice Worksheet

### Perpendicular Vectors

*Find each inner product and state whether the vectors are perpendicular. Write yes or no.*

**1.** $(3, 6) \cdot (-4, 2)$
   **0; yes**

**2.** $(-1, 4) \cdot (3, -2)$
   **−11; no**

**3.** $(2, 0) \cdot (-1, -1)$
   **−2; no**

**4.** $(7, -3) \cdot (-2, 4)$
   **−26; no**

**5.** $(-3, 0) \cdot (4, -3)$
   **−12; no**

**6.** $(7, -4) \cdot (-5, -8)$
   **−3; no**

**7.** $(-2, 0, 1) \cdot (3, 2, -3)$
   **−9; no**

**8.** $(-4, -1, 1) \cdot (1, -3, 4)$
   **3; no**

**9.** $(0, 0, 1) \cdot (1, -2, 0)$
   **0; yes**

*Find each cross product. Then verify that the resulting vector is perpendicular to the given vectors.*

**10.** $(1, 3, 4) \times (-1, 0, -1)$
   **(−3, −3, 3); yes**

**11.** $(3, 1, -6) \times (-2, 4, 3)$
   **(27, 3, 14); yes**

**12.** $(3, 1, 2) \times (2, -3, 1)$
   **(7, 1, −11); yes**

**13.** $(4, -1, 0) \times (5, -3, -1)$
   **(1, 4, −7); yes**

**14.** $(-6, 1, 3) \times (-2, -2, 1)$
   **(7, 0, 14); yes**

**15.** $(0, 0, 6) \times (3, -2, -4)$
   **(12, 18, 0); yes**

# 8-5 Practice Worksheet

## Applications with Vectors

*Solve. Make a diagram to help you. Round all angle measures to the nearest minute. Round all other measures to the nearest tenth.*

1. A plane flies due west at 250 kilometers per hour while the wind blows south at 70 kilometers per hour. Find the plane's resultant velocity and direction.

2. A plane flies east for 200 km, then 60° south of east for 80 km. Find the plane's distance and direction from its starting point.

3. One force of 100 units acts on an object. Another force of 80 units acts on the object at a 40° angle from the first force. Find the magnitude and direction of the resultant force on the object.

Glencoe Division, Macmillan/McGraw-Hill

# 8-5  Practice Worksheet

## Applications with Vectors

**Solve. Make a diagram to help you. Round all angle measures to the nearest minute. Round all other measures to the nearest tenth.**

1. A plane flies due west at 250 kilometers per hour while the wind blows south at 70 kilometers per hour. Find the plane's resultant velocity and direction.

   **259.6 km/hr; 15°39′ south of west**

2. A plane flies east for 200 km, then 60° south of east for 80 km. Find the plane's distance and direction from its starting point.

   **249.83 km; 16°6′ south of east**

3. One force of 100 units acts on an object. Another force of 80 units acts on the object at a 40° angle from the first force. Find the magnitude and direction of the resultant force on the object.

   **169.3 units; 17°41′ from the first force**

Glencoe Division, Macmillan/McGraw-Hill

## 8-6 Practice Worksheet

## Vectors and Parametric Equations

*Write a vector equation of the line that passes through point P and is parallel to ā.*
*Then write parametric equations for the line.*

1. $P(-2, 1), \bar{a} = (3, -4)$ 

2. $P(3, 7), \bar{a} = (4, 5)$

3. $P(2, -4), \bar{a} = (1, 3)$ 

4. $P(5, -8), \bar{a} = (9, 2)$

*Write the equation of each line in parametric form.*

5. $y = 3x - 8$ 

6. $y = -x + 4$

7. $3x - 2y = 6$ 

8. $5x + 4y = 20$

*Write an equation in slope-intercept form of the line with the given parametric equations.*

9. $x = 2t + 3$
   $y = t - 4$

10. $x = t + 5$
    $y = -3t$

11. $x = t + 4$
    $y = t - 9$

12. $x = 7t + 3$
    $y = -6t + 8$

*Set up a table of values and then graph each line from its parametric form.*

13. $x = 5t + 3$
    $y = -2t + 7$

14. $x = 3t - 9$
    $y = -2t + 5$

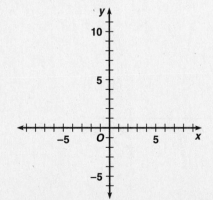
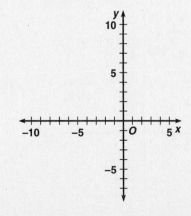

Glencoe Division, Macmillan/McGraw-Hill

8-6

# Practice Worksheet

## Vectors and Parametric Equations

*Write a vector equation of the line that passes through point P and is parallel to $\vec{a}$.*
*Then write parametric equations for the line.*

**1.** $P(-2, 1), \vec{a} = (3, -4)$
$(x + 2, y - 1) = t(3, -4)$
$x = -2 + 3t$
$y = 1 - 4t$

**2.** $P(3, 7), \vec{a} = (4, 5)$
$(x - 3, y - 7) = t(4, 5)$
$x = 3 + 4t$
$y = 7 + 5t$

**3.** $P(2, -4), \vec{a} = (1, 3)$
$(x - 2, y + 4) = t(1, 3)$
$x = 2 + t$
$y = -4 + 3t$

**4.** $P(5, -8), \vec{a} = (9, 2)$
$(x - 5, y + 8) = t(9, 2)$
$x = 5 + 9t$
$y = -8 + 2t$

*Write the equation of each line in parametric form.*

**5.** $y = 3x - 8$
$x = t$
$y = 3t - 8$

**6.** $y = -x + 4$
$x = t$
$y = -t + 4$

**7.** $3x - 2y = 6$
$x = t$
$y = \dfrac{3}{2}t - 3$

**8.** $5x + 4y = 20$
$x = t$
$y = -\dfrac{5}{4}t + 5$

*Write an equation in slope-intercept form of the line with the given parametric equations.*

**9.** $x = 2t + 3$ $\quad y = \dfrac{1}{2}x - \dfrac{11}{2}$
$\phantom{xx}y = t - 4$

**10.** $x = t + 5$ $\quad y = -3x + 15$
$\phantom{xxx}y = -3t$

**11.** $x = t + 4$ $\quad y = x - 13$
$\phantom{xx}y = t - 9$

**12.** $x = 7t + 3$ $\quad y = -\dfrac{6}{7}x + \dfrac{74}{7}$
$\phantom{xxx}y = -6t + 8$

*Set up a table of values and then graph each line from its parametric form.*

**13.** $x = 5t + 3$
$\phantom{xx}y = -2t + 7$

**14.** $x = 3t - 9$
$\phantom{xx}y = -2t + 5$

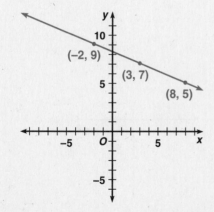

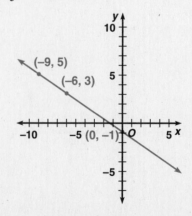

Glencoe Division, Macmillan/McGraw-Hill

## 8-7 Practice Worksheet

### Using Parametric Equations to Model Motion

*For each exercise,*
*a) write parametric equations to represent the path of the object,*
*b) graph the path, and*
*c) solve.*
*Round your answers to the nearest hundredth.*

1. A rock is tossed at an initial velocity of 50 m/s at an angle of 8° with the ground. After 0.8 seconds, how far has the rock traveled horizontally and vertically?

2. A toy rocket is launched at an initial velocity of 80 ft/s at an angle of 80° with the horizontal. How long will it take for the rocket to be 10 feet horizontally from its starting point. What will its vertical distance be at that point?

3. A bullet is shot at a target 200 feet away. If the bullet is shot at a height of 5 feet, with an initial velocity of 150 ft/s, and at an angle of 10° with the horizontal, when will it reach the target, and what will be the height where it hits?

4. A disk is thrown from a height of 5 meters at an initial velocity of 65 m/s at an angle of 10° with the ground. After 0.5 second, how far has the disk traveled horizontally and vertically?

**8-7**

# Practice Worksheet

## *Using Parametric Equations to Model Motion*

*For each exercise,*
*a) write parametric equations to represent the path of the object,*
*b) graph the path, and*
*c) solve.*
*Round your answers to the nearest hundredth.*

1. A rock is tossed at an initial velocity of 50 m/s at an angle of 8° with the ground. After 0.8 seconds, how far has the rock traveled horizontally and vertically?

   **a)** $x = 50t \cos 8°$;
       $y = 50t \sin 8° - 4.9t^2$
   **c)** $x \approx 39.61$ m; $y \approx 2.43$ m

   **b)**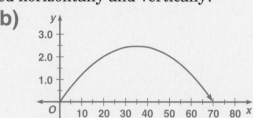

2. A toy rocket is launched at an initial velocity of 80 ft/s at an angle of 80° with the horizontal. How long will it take for the rocket to be 10 feet horizontally from its starting point. What will its vertical distance be at that point?

   **a)** $x = 80t \cos 80°$;
       $y = 80t \sin 80° - 16t^2$
   **c)** 0.72 s; 48.43 ft

   **b)**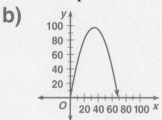

3. A bullet is shot at a target 200 feet away. If the bullet is shot at a height of 5 feet, with an initial velocity of 150 ft/s, and at an angle of 10° with the horizontal, when will it reach the target, and what will be the height where it hits?

   **a)** $x = 150t \cos 10°$;
       $y = 150t \sin 10° - 16t^2 + 5$
   **c)** 1.35 s; 11.00 ft

   **b)**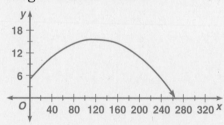

4. A disk is thrown from a height of 5 meters at an initial velocity of 65 m/s at an angle of 10° with the ground. After 0.5 second, how far has the disk traveled horizontally and vertically?

   **a)** $x = 65t \cos 10°$;
       $y = 150t \sin 10° - 16t^2 + 5$
   **c)** 32.01 m; 9.42 m

   **b)**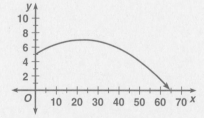

Glencoe Division, Macmillan/McGraw-Hill

# Practice Worksheet

## Polar Coordinates

**Graph the point that has the given polar coordinates.**

**1.** $(2.5, 0°)$

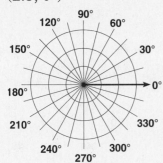

**2.** $(3, -135°)$

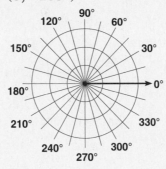

**3.** $(-1, -30°)$

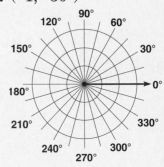

**4.** $\left(-2, \dfrac{\pi}{4}\right)$

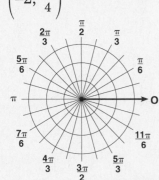

**5.** $\left(1, \dfrac{5\pi}{4}\right)$

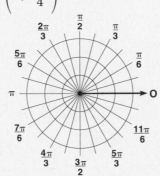

**6.** $\left(1, -\dfrac{2\pi}{3}\right)$

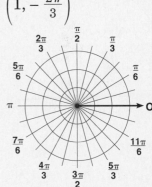

**Name four different pairs of polar coordinates that represent point A.**

**7.**

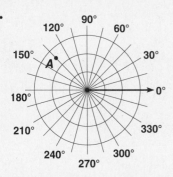

**8.**

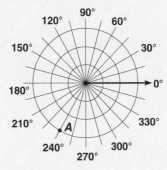

**Graph each polar equation.**

**9.** $r = 3$

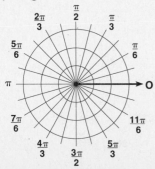

**10.** $\theta = 60°$

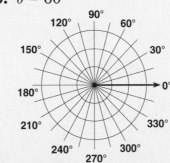

Glencoe Division, Macmillan/McGraw-Hill

# Practice Worksheet

## Polar Coordinates

**Graph the point that has the given polar coordinates.**

**1.** $(2.5, 0°)$

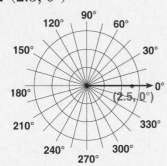

**2.** $(3, -135°)$

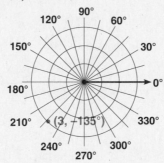

**3.** $(-1, -30°)$

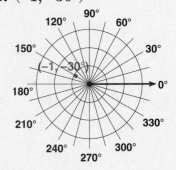

**4.** $\left(-2, \dfrac{\pi}{4}\right)$

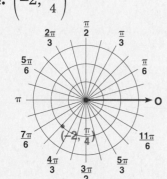

**5.** $\left(1, \dfrac{5\pi}{4}\right)$

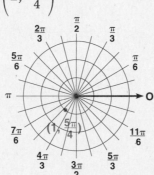

**6.** $\left(1, -\dfrac{2\pi}{3}\right)$

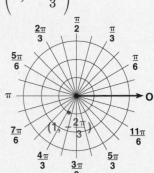

Answers will vary. Sample answers are given.

**Name four different pairs of polar coordinates that represent point A.**

**7.**

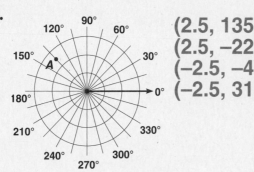

(2.5, 135°)
(2.5, −225°)
(−2.5, −45°)
(−2.5, 315°)

**8.**

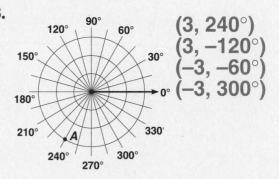

(3, 240°)
(3, −120°)
(−3, −60°)
(−3, 300°)

**Graph each polar equation.**

**9.** $r = 3$

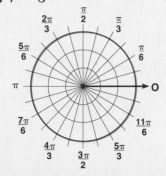

**10.** $\theta = 60°$

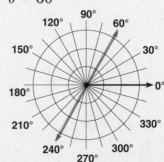

Glencoe Division, Macmillan/McGraw-Hill

**9-2**

# Practice Worksheet

## Graphs of Polar Equations

*Graph each polar equation. Identify the classical curve it represents.*

**1.** $r = 2 + 2\cos\theta$

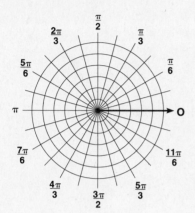

**2.** $r = 3\sin 3\theta$

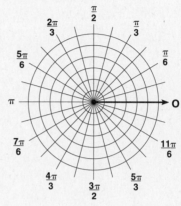

**3.** $r = 2 + 3\cos\theta$

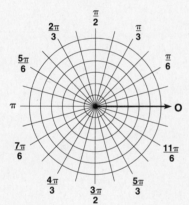

**4.** $r = 2 + 2\sin\theta$

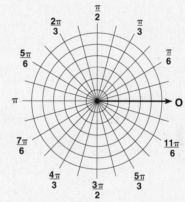

**5.** $r = \theta$

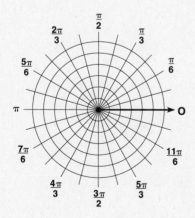

**6.** $r^2 = 5\cos 2\theta$

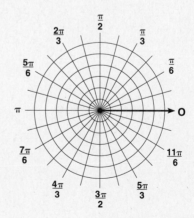

Glencoe Division, Macmillan/McGraw-Hill

**9-2**

# Practice Worksheet

## Graphs of Polar Equations

*Graph each polar equation. Identify the classical curve it represents.*

**1.** $r = 2 + 2\cos\theta$
**cardioid**

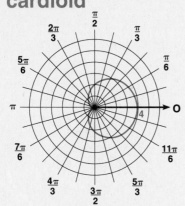

**2.** $r = 3\sin 3\theta$
**rose**

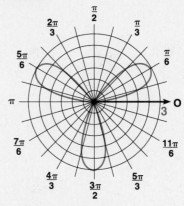

**3.** $r = 2 + 3\cos\theta$
**limaçon**

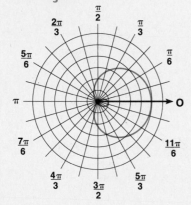

**4.** $r = 2 + 2\sin\theta$
**cardioid**

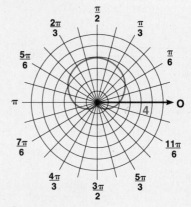

**5.** $r = \theta$
**spiral of Archimedes**

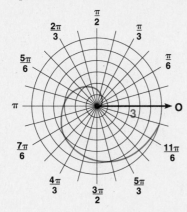

**6.** $r^2 = 5\cos 2\theta$
**lemniscate**

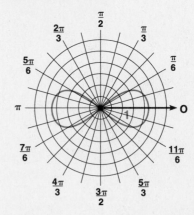

# 9-3 Practice Worksheet

## Polar and Rectangular Coordinates

**Find the polar coordinates of each point with the given rectangular coordinates.**

**1.** $(0, 4)$

**2.** $\left(\frac{1}{2}, -\frac{\sqrt{3}}{2}\right)$

**3.** $\left(-\frac{\sqrt{3}}{2}, \frac{1}{2}\right)$

**4.** $(4, 0)$

**5.** $(-1, -\sqrt{3})$

**6.** $(2, 2)$

**Find the rectangular coordinates of each point with the given polar coordinates.**

**7.** $(6, 120°)$

**8.** $(-4, 45°)$

**9.** $(3, 300°)$

**10.** $\left(4, \frac{\pi}{6}\right)$

**11.** $\left(0, \frac{13\pi}{3}\right)$

**12.** $\left(3, -\frac{3\pi}{4}\right)$

**Write each rectangular equation in polar form.**

**13.** $x^2 + y^2 = 9$

**14.** $y = 3$

**15.** $x^2 - y^2 = 1$

**16.** $x^2 + y^2 - 2y = 0$

**Write each polar equation in rectangular form.**

**17.** $r = 4$

**18.** $\theta = -\frac{\pi}{3}$

**19.** $r \cos \theta = 5$

**20.** $r = -3 \sec \theta$

Glencoe Division, Macmillan/McGraw-Hill

**9-3** # Practice Worksheet

## Polar and Rectangular Coordinates

**Find the polar coordinates of each point with the given rectangular coordinates.**

**1.** $(0, 4)$

$\left(4, \frac{\pi}{2}\right)$

**2.** $\left(\frac{1}{2}, -\frac{\sqrt{3}}{2}\right)$

$\left(1, -\frac{\pi}{3}\right)$

**3.** $\left(-\frac{\sqrt{3}}{2}, \frac{1}{2}\right)$

$\left(1, \frac{5\pi}{6}\right)$

**4.** $(4, 0)$

$(4, 0)$

**5.** $(-1, -\sqrt{3})$

$\left(2, \frac{4\pi}{3}\right)$

**6.** $(2, 2)$

$\left(2\sqrt{2}, \frac{\pi}{4}\right)$

**Find the rectangular coordinates of each point with the given polar coordinates.**

**7.** $(6, 120°)$

$(-3, 3\sqrt{3})$

**8.** $(-4, 45°)$

$(-2\sqrt{2}, -2\sqrt{2})$

**9.** $(3, 300°)$

$\left(\frac{3}{2}, -\frac{3\sqrt{3}}{2}\right)$

**10.** $\left(4, \frac{\pi}{6}\right)$

$(2\sqrt{3}, 2)$

**11.** $\left(0, \frac{13\pi}{3}\right)$

$(0, 0)$

**12.** $\left(3, -\frac{3\pi}{4}\right)$

$\left(-\frac{3\sqrt{2}}{2}, -\frac{3\sqrt{2}}{2}\right)$

**Write each rectangular equation in polar form.**

**13.** $x^2 + y^2 = 9$
$r = \pm 3$

**14.** $y = 3$
$r \sin \theta = 3$ or $r = 3 \csc \theta$

**15.** $x^2 - y^2 = 1$
$r^2 = \dfrac{1}{\cos 2\theta} = \sec 2\theta$

**16.** $x^2 + y^2 - 2y = 0$
$r = 2 \sin \theta$

**Write each polar equation in rectangular form.**

**17.** $r = 4$
$x^2 + y^2 = 16$

**18.** $\theta = -\frac{\pi}{3}$
$y = -\sqrt{3}x$

**19.** $r \cos \theta = 5$
$x = 5$

**20.** $r = -3 \sec \theta$
$x = -3$

Glencoe Division, Macmillan/McGraw-Hill

# Practice Worksheet

## Polar Form of a Linear Function

**Graph each polar equation.**

**1.** $1 = r \cos(\theta - 30°)$

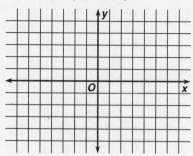

**2.** $3 = r \cos(\theta + 60°)$

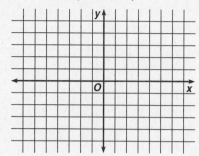

**3.** $2.5 = r \cos(\theta + 30°)$

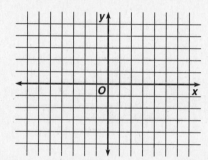

**4.** $r = \dfrac{1.5}{\cos(\theta + 90°)}$

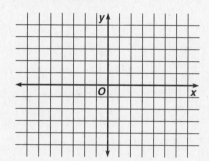

**Write each equation in polar form. Round $\phi$ to the nearest degree.**

**5.** $y + x = 0$

**6.** $y = 2x - 1$

**7.** $2 = y - 2x$

**8.** $x = 11$

**Write each equation in rectangular form.**

**9.** $r \cos\left(\theta + \dfrac{\pi}{3}\right) = 1$

**10.** $r = \dfrac{2}{\cos\theta}$

**11.** $r \cos\left(\theta - \dfrac{3\pi}{4}\right) - 2 = 0$

**12.** $r \cos\left(\theta - \dfrac{\pi}{4}\right) - 3 = 0$

**9-4**

# Practice Worksheet

## Polar Form of a Linear Function

**Graph each polar equation.**

**1.** $1 = r \cos (\theta - 30°)$

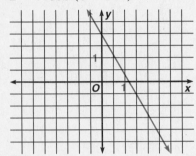

**2.** $3 = r \cos (\theta + 60°)$

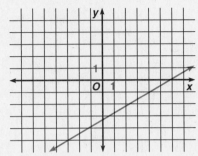

**3.** $2.5 = r \cos (\theta + 30°)$

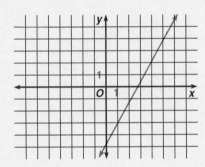

**4.** $r = \dfrac{1.5}{\cos (\theta + 90°)}$

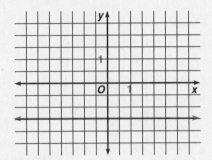

**Write each equation in polar form. Round $\phi$ to the nearest degree.**

**5.** $y + x = 0$

$$0 = r \cos (\theta - 45°)$$

**6.** $y = 2x - 1$

$$\frac{\sqrt{5}}{5} = r \cos (\theta - 333°)$$

**7.** $2 = y - 2x$

$$\frac{2\sqrt{5}}{5} = r \cos (\theta - 153°)$$

**8.** $x = 11$

$$11 = r \cos \theta$$

**Write each equation in rectangular form.**

**9.** $r \cos \left( \theta + \dfrac{\pi}{3} \right) = 1$

$$x + (-\sqrt{3})y - 2 = 0$$

**10.** $r = \dfrac{2}{\cos \theta}$

$$x - 2 = 0$$

**11.** $r \cos \left( \theta - \dfrac{3\pi}{4} \right) - 2 = 0$

$$(-\sqrt{2})x + (\sqrt{2})y - 4 = 0$$

**12.** $r \cos \left( \theta - \dfrac{\pi}{4} \right) - 3 = 0$

$$(\sqrt{2})x + (\sqrt{2}) y - 6 = 0$$

Glencoe Division, Macmillan/McGraw-Hill

# 9-5 Practice Worksheet

## Simplifying Complex Numbers

**Simplify.**

**1.** $i^{65} + i^{29}$

**2.** $i^{243}(1 - 3i)$

**3.** $(3 + 2i) + (4 + 5i)$

**4.** $(-6 - 2i) - (-8 - 3i)$

**5.** $(2 - 3i)(5 + i)$

**6.** $(\sqrt{2} + 2i)(\sqrt{2} - 2i)$

**7.** $(3 + 4i)^2$

**8.** $(3 + \sqrt{-5})(3 + \sqrt{-5})$

**9.** $\dfrac{4 - 7i}{-3i}$

**10.** $\dfrac{4 + 3i}{1 - 2i}$

**11.** $\dfrac{2}{6 + 5i}$

**12.** $(6 - i)^2$

**13.** $\dfrac{4}{\sqrt{3} + 2i}$

**14.** $\dfrac{7}{\sqrt{2} - 3i}$

**Find values for x and y that make each sentence true.**

**15.** $3x - 7yi = 21 - 56i$

**16.** $7x + 8yi = 49 - 64i$

## 9-5 Practice Worksheet

### Simplifying Complex Numbers

**Simplify.**

1. $i^{65} + i^{29}$
   **2i**

2. $i^{243}(1 - 3i)$
   **−3 − i**

3. $(3 + 2i) + (4 + 5i)$
   **7 + 7i**

4. $(-6 - 2i) - (-8 - 3i)$
   **2 + i**

5. $(2 - 3i)(5 + i)$
   **13 − 13i**

6. $(\sqrt{2} + 2i)(\sqrt{2} - 2i)$
   **6**

7. $(3 + 4i)^2$
   **−7 + 24i**

8. $(3 + \sqrt{-5})(3 + \sqrt{-5})$
   **4 + 6√5i**

9. $\dfrac{4 - 7i}{-3i}$
   $\dfrac{7}{3} + \dfrac{4}{3}i$

10. $\dfrac{4 + 3i}{1 - 2i}$
    $-\dfrac{2}{5} + \dfrac{11}{5}i$

11. $\dfrac{2}{6 + 5i}$
    $\dfrac{12}{61} - \dfrac{10}{61}i$

12. $(6 - i)^2$
    **35 − 12i**

13. $\dfrac{4}{\sqrt{3} + 2i}$
    $\dfrac{4\sqrt{3}}{7} - \dfrac{8}{7}i$

14. $\dfrac{7}{\sqrt{2} - 3i}$
    $\dfrac{7\sqrt{2}}{11} + \dfrac{21}{11}i$

**Find values for x and y that make each sentence true.**

15. $3x - 7yi = 21 - 56i$
    **x = 7, y = 8**

16. $7x + 8yi = 49 - 64i$
    **x = 7, y = −8**

Glencoe Division, Macmillan/McGraw-Hill

NAME _____ DATE _____

# Practice Worksheet

## Polar Form of Complex Numbers

**Express each complex number in polar form.**

1. $3 + 3\sqrt{3}i$

2. $7i$

3. $-\sqrt{3} + i$

4. $4$

5. $1 - i$

6. $-1 + i$

7. $\sqrt{2} - \sqrt{2}i$

8. $-\sqrt{2} + \sqrt{2}i$

9. $2\sqrt{3} + 2i$

10. $1.5 + 1.5i$

11. $5 - 5\sqrt{3}i$

12. $-\frac{1}{2} - \frac{\sqrt{3}}{2}i$

**Express each complex number in rectangular form.**

13. $2\left(\cos \frac{3\pi}{4} + i \sin \frac{3\pi}{4}\right)$

14. $\sqrt{2}\left(\cos \frac{3\pi}{2} + i \sin \frac{3\pi}{2}\right)$

15. $1.5\left(\cos \frac{\pi}{6} + i \sin \frac{\pi}{6}\right)$

16. $4\left(\cos \frac{5\pi}{6} + i \sin \frac{5\pi}{6}\right)$

17. $4\left(\cos \frac{7\pi}{6} + i \sin \frac{7\pi}{6}\right)$

18. $3\left(\cos \frac{11\pi}{4} + i \sin \frac{11\pi}{4}\right)$

# Practice Worksheet

## Polar Form of Complex Numbers

**Express each complex number in polar form.**

1. $3 + 3\sqrt{3}i$
   $6(\cos 60° + i \sin 60°)$

2. $7i$
   $7(\cos 90° + i \sin 90°)$

3. $-\sqrt{3} + i$
   $2(\cos 150° + i \sin 150°)$

4. $4$
   $4(\cos 0° + i \sin 0°)$

5. $1 - i$
   $\sqrt{2}(\cos 315° + i \sin 315°)$

6. $-1 \pm i$
   $\sqrt{2}(\cos 135° + i \sin 135°)$

7. $\sqrt{2} - \sqrt{2}i$
   $2(\cos 315° + i \sin 315°)$

8. $-\sqrt{2} + \sqrt{2}i$
   $2(\cos 135° + i \sin 135°)$

9. $2\sqrt{3} + 2i$
   $4(\cos 30° + i \sin 30°)$

10. $1.5 + 1.5i$
    $\sqrt{4.5}(\cos 45° + i \sin 45°)$

11. $5 - 5\sqrt{3}i$

    $10(\cos 300° + i \sin 300°)$

12. $-\dfrac{1}{2} - \dfrac{\sqrt{3}}{2}i$

    $\cos 240° + i \sin 240°$

**Express each complex number in rectangular form.**

13. $2\left(\cos \dfrac{3\pi}{4} + i \sin \dfrac{3\pi}{4}\right)$
    $-\sqrt{2} + \sqrt{2}i$

14. $\sqrt{2}\left(\cos \dfrac{3\pi}{2} + i \sin \dfrac{3\pi}{2}\right)$
    $-\sqrt{2}i$

15. $1.5\left(\cos \dfrac{\pi}{6} + i \sin \dfrac{\pi}{6}\right)$
    $\dfrac{3\sqrt{3}}{4} + \dfrac{3}{4}i$

16. $4\left(\cos \dfrac{5\pi}{6} + i \sin \dfrac{5\pi}{6}\right)$
    $-2\sqrt{3} + 2i$

17. $4\left(\cos \dfrac{7\pi}{6} + i \sin \dfrac{7\pi}{6}\right)$

    $-2\sqrt{3} - 2i$

18. $3\left(\cos \dfrac{11\pi}{4} + i \sin \dfrac{11\pi}{4}\right)$

    $-\dfrac{3\sqrt{2}}{2} + \dfrac{3\sqrt{2}}{2}i$

Glencoe Division, Macmillan/McGraw-Hill

# 9-7 Practice Worksheet

## Products and Quotients of Complex Numbers in Polar Form

*Find each product or quotient.*

**1.** $(3 - 2i)(4 + i)$

**2.** $(4 - i) \div (2 + 2i)$

**3.** $(4 - \sqrt{3}i) \div (2 + \sqrt{3}i)$

**4.** $(\sqrt{3} - 2i)(4\sqrt{3} + i)$

*Find each product or quotient. Then write the result in rectangular form.*

**5.** $3\left(\cos \frac{\pi}{3} + i \sin \frac{\pi}{3}\right) \cdot 3\left(\cos \frac{5\pi}{3} + i \sin \frac{5\pi}{3}\right)$

**6.** $4.5\left(\cos \frac{\pi}{3} + i \sin \frac{\pi}{3}\right) \div 3\left(\cos \frac{\pi}{4} + i \sin \frac{\pi}{4}\right)$

**7.** $7\left(\cos \frac{5\pi}{6} + i \sin \frac{5\pi}{6}\right) \div 14\left(\cos \frac{\pi}{4} + i \sin \frac{\pi}{4}\right)$

**8.** $3\left(\cos \frac{7\pi}{4} + i \sin \frac{7\pi}{4}\right)2 \cdot \left(\cos \frac{4\pi}{3} + i \sin \frac{4\pi}{3}\right)$

**9.** $18\left(\cos \frac{5\pi}{6} + i \sin \frac{5\pi}{6}\right) \cdot 6\left(\cos \frac{5\pi}{3} + i \sin \frac{5\pi}{3}\right)$

**9-7**

# Practice Worksheet

## Products and Quotients of Complex Numbers in Polar Form

**Find each product or quotient.**

**1.** $(3 - 2i)(4 + i)$

$14 - 5i$

**2.** $(4 - i) \div (2 + 2i)$

$\dfrac{3}{4} - \dfrac{5}{4}i$

**3.** $(4 - \sqrt{3}i) \div (2 + \sqrt{3}i)$

$\dfrac{5}{7} - \dfrac{6\sqrt{3}}{7}i$

**4.** $(\sqrt{3} - 2i)(4\sqrt{3} + i)$

$14 - 7\sqrt{3}i$

**Find each product or quotient. Then write the result in rectangular form.**

**5.** $3\left(\cos \dfrac{\pi}{3} + i \sin \dfrac{\pi}{3}\right) \cdot 3\left(\cos \dfrac{5\pi}{3} + i \sin \dfrac{5\pi}{3}\right)$

$9(\cos 2\pi + i \sin 2\pi);\ 9$

**6.** $4.5\left(\cos \dfrac{\pi}{3} + i \sin \dfrac{\pi}{3}\right) \div 3\left(\cos \dfrac{\pi}{4} + i \sin \dfrac{\pi}{4}\right)$

$1.5\left(\cos \dfrac{7\pi}{12} + i \sin \dfrac{7\pi}{12}\right);\ 1.45 + 0.39i$

**7.** $7\left(\cos \dfrac{5\pi}{6} + i \sin \dfrac{5\pi}{6}\right) \div 14\left(\cos \dfrac{\pi}{4} + i \sin \dfrac{\pi}{4}\right)$

$\dfrac{1}{2}\left(\cos \dfrac{13\pi}{12} + i \sin \dfrac{13\pi}{12}\right);\ -0.13 + 0.48i$

**8.** $3\left(\cos \dfrac{7\pi}{4} + i \sin \dfrac{7\pi}{4}\right)2 \cdot \left(\cos \dfrac{4\pi}{3} + i \sin \dfrac{4\pi}{3}\right)$

$6\left(\cos \dfrac{37\pi}{12} + i \sin \dfrac{37\pi}{12}\right);\ -5.80 - 1.55i$

**9.** $18\left(\cos \dfrac{5\pi}{6} + i \sin \dfrac{5\pi}{6}\right) \cdot 6\left(\cos \dfrac{5\pi}{3} + i \sin \dfrac{5\pi}{3}\right)$

$108\left(\cos \dfrac{5\pi}{2} + i \sin \dfrac{5\pi}{2}\right);\ 108i$

# Practice Worksheet

## Powers and Roots of Complex Numbers

**Find each power. Express the result in rectangular form.**

**1.** $(1 - i)^5$

**2.** $(2 - 2i\sqrt{3})^5$

**3.** $(-2 - 2i\sqrt{3})^3$

**4.** $(1 + i)^8$

**5.** $(\sqrt{2}(1 + i))^6$

**6.** $\left( \frac{\sqrt{2}}{2} - \frac{\sqrt{2}}{2} i \right)^5$

**Find each root. Express the result in the form a + bi, with a and b to the nearest hundredth.**

**7.** $(0 - 27i)^{\frac{1}{3}}$

**8.** $(8 - 8i)^{\frac{1}{3}}$

**9.** $\sqrt[5]{-243i}$

**10.** $(0 - i)^{-\frac{1}{3}}$

**11.** $\sqrt[8]{-8i}$

**12.** $\sqrt[4]{-2 - 2i\sqrt{3}}$

Glencoe Division, Macmillan/McGraw-Hill

## 9-8 Practice Worksheet

### Powers and Roots of Complex Numbers

Find each power. Express the result in rectangular form.

1. $(1 - i)^5$
$-4 + 4i$

2. $(2 - 2i\sqrt{3})^5$
$512 + 512i\sqrt{3}$

3. $(-2 - 2i\sqrt{3})^3$
$64$

4. $(1 + i)^8$
$16$

5. $(\sqrt{2}(1 + i))^6$

$-64i$

6. $\left(\dfrac{\sqrt{2}}{2} - \dfrac{\sqrt{2}}{2}i\right)^5$

$-\dfrac{\sqrt{2}}{2} + \dfrac{\sqrt{2}}{2}i$

Find each root. Express the result in the form a + bi, with a and b to the nearest hundredth.

7. $(0 - 27i)^{\frac{1}{3}}$
$3i$

8. $(8 - 8i)^{\frac{1}{3}}$
$2.17 - 0.58i$

9. $\sqrt[5]{-243i}$
$1.76 + 2.43i$

10. $(0 - i)^{-\frac{1}{3}}$
$-i$

11. $\sqrt[8]{-8i}$
$1.08 + 0.72i$

12. $\sqrt[4]{-2 - 2i\sqrt{3}}$
$0.71 + 1.22i$

Glencoe Division, Macmillan/McGraw-Hill

# 10-1 Practice Worksheet

## The Circle

**Write the standard form of each equation. Then graph the equation**

**1.** $x^2 + y^2 - 2y - 15 = 0$

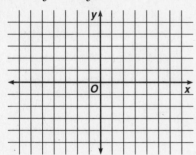

**2.** $x^2 + 4x + y^2 = 0$

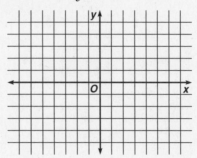

**3.** $x^2 + y^2 - 8x - 6y + 21 = 0$

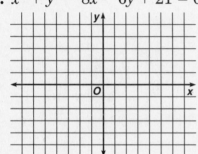

**4.** $4x^2 + 4y^2 - 16x - 8y - 5 = 0$

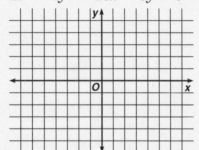

*Write the standard form of the equation of the circle that passes through the points with the given coordinates. Then identify the center and the radius of the circle.*

**5.** $(-3, -2), (-2, -3), (-4, -3)$

**6.** $(0, -1), (2, -3), (4, -1)$

**7.** $(1, -1), (5, 3), (-3, 3)$

**8.** $(-1, 0), (2, 3), (-1, 6)$

**9.** Write the equation of the circle that passes through $(-1, 3)$ and has its center at $(2, 4)$.

Glencoe Division, Macmillan/McGraw-Hill

# Practice Worksheet

## The Circle

*Write the standard form of each equation. Then graph the equation*

**1.** $x^2 + y^2 - 2y - 15 = 0$

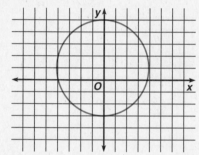

$$x^2 + (y - 1)^2 = 16$$

**2.** $x^2 + 4x + y^2 = 0$

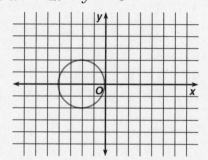

$$(x + 2)^2 + y^2 = 4$$

**3.** $x^2 + y^2 - 8x - 6y + 21 = 0$

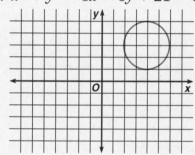

$$(x - 4)^2 + (y - 3)^2 = 4$$

**4.** $4x^2 + 4y^2 - 16x - 8y - 5 = 0$

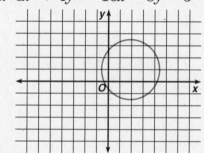

$$(x + 2)^2 + (y - 1)^2 = \frac{25}{4}$$

*Write the standard form of the equation of the circle that passes through the points with the given coordinates. Then identify the center and the radius of the circle.*

**5.** $(-3, -2), (-2, -3), (-4, -3)$
$$(x + 3)^2 + (y + 3)^2 = 1;$$
$$(-3, -3); 1$$

**6.** $(0, -1), (2, -3), (4, -1)$
$$(x - 2)^2 + (y + 1)^2 = 4;$$
$$(2, -1); 2$$

**7.** $(1, -1), (5, 3), (-3, 3)$
$$(x - 1)^2 + (y - 3)^2 = 16;$$
$$(1, 3); 4$$

**8.** $(-1, 0), (2, 3), (-1, 6)$
$$(x + 1)^2 + (y - 3)^2 = 9;$$
$$(-1, 3); 3$$

**9.** Write the equation of the circle that passes through $(-1, 3)$ and has its center at $(2, 4)$.

$$(x - 2)^2 + (y - 4)^2 = 10$$

Glencoe Division, Macmillan/McGraw-Hill

# 10-2 Practice Worksheet

## The Parabola

**For each equation,**

a. write the standard form,
b. find the coordinates of the focus and vertex, and the equation of the directrix and axis of symmetry, and
c. graph the equation.

**1.** $x^2 - 2x + 1 = 8y - 16$

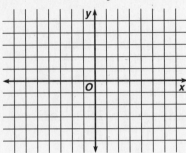

**2.** $y^2 + 6y + 9 = 16 - 16x$

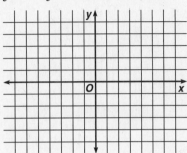

**Write the equation of the parabola that meets each set of conditions. Then graph the equation.**

**3.** The parabola has its focus at $(1, 3)$ and the vertex at $(1, 2)$.

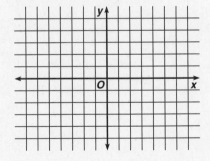

**4.** The focus is at $(2, 1)$, and the equation of the directrix is $x = -2$.

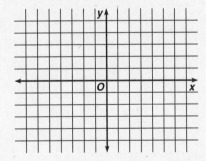

## 10-2 Practice Worksheet

## The Parabola

*For each equation,*

a. write the standard form,
b. find the coordinates of the focus and vertex, and the equation of the directrix and axis of symmetry, and
c. graph the equation.

**1.** $x^2 - 2x + 1 = 8y - 16$

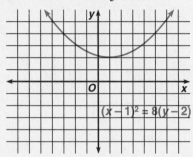

$(x - 1)^2 = 8(y - 2)$;
focus: (1, 4); vertex: (1, 2);
directrix: $y = 0$;
axis of symmetry: $x = 1$

**2.** $y^2 + 6y + 9 = 16 - 16x$

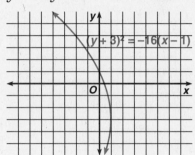

$(y + 3)^2 = -16(x - 1)$;
focus: (–3, –3); vertex: (1, –3);
directrix: $x = 5$;
axis of symmetry: $y = 3$

*Write the equation of the parabola that meets each set of conditions. Then graph the equation.*

**3.** The parabola has its focus at (1, 3) and the vertex at (1, 2).

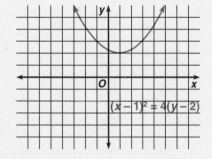

$(x - 1)^2 = 4(y - 2)$

**4.** The focus is at (2, 1), and the equation of the directrix is $x = -2$.

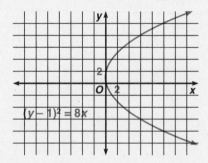

$(y - 1)^2 = 8x$

Glencoe Division, Macmillan/McGraw-Hill

# 10-3 Practice Worksheet

## The Ellipse

*For each equation, find the coordinates of the center, foci, and vertices of the ellipse. Then graph the equation.*

**1.** $4x^2 + y^2 - 32x + 4y + 64 = 0$

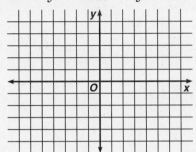

**2.** $4x^2 + 9y^2 - 8x - 36y + 4 = 0$

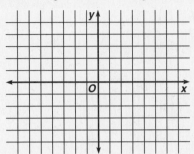

*Write the equation of the ellipse that meets each set of conditions.*

**3.** The foci are at $(-2, 1)$ and $(-2, -7)$, and $a = 5$.

**4.** The length of the semi-major axis is 6 units, and the foci are at $(0, 2)$ and $(8, 2)$.

**5.** The center is at $(1, 3)$, one vertex is at $(1, 8)$, and $\frac{c}{a} = \frac{4}{5}$.

*State whether the graph of each equation is a circle, parabola, or ellipse. Justify your answer.*

**6.** $x^2 + 4y^2 - 2x - 16y + 1 = 0$

**7.** $x^2 + 4y - 16 = 0$

**8.** $x^2 + y^2 + 6x + 2y + 7 = 0$

**9.** $4x^2 + 4y^2 - 20x - 24 = 0$

Glencoe Division, Macmillan/McGraw-Hill

## 10-3 Practice Worksheet

### The Ellipse

*For each equation, find the coordinates of the center, foci, and vertices of the ellipse. Then graph the equation.*

1. $4x^2 + y^2 - 32x + 4y + 64 = 0$

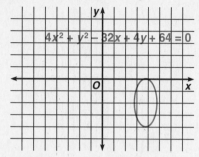

center: (4, –2);
foci: $(4, -2 \pm \sqrt{3})$;
vertices: (4, 0), (4, –4), (3, –2), (5, –2)

2. $4x^2 + 9y^2 - 8x - 36y + 4 = 0$

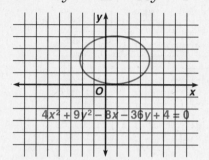

center: (1, 2);
foci: $(1 \pm \sqrt{5}, 2)$;
vertices: (–2, 2), (1, 4), (4, 2), (1, 0)

*Write the equation of the ellipse that meets each set of conditions.*

3. The foci are at (–2, 1) and (–2, –7), and $a = 5$.

$$\frac{(y+3)^2}{25} + \frac{(x+2)^2}{9} = 1$$

4. The length of the semi-major axis is 6 units, and the foci are at (0,2) and (8, 2).

$$\frac{(x-4)^2}{36} + \frac{(y-2)^2}{20} = 1$$

5. The center is at (1, 3), one vertex is at (1, 8), and $\frac{c}{a} = \frac{4}{5}$.

$$\frac{(y-3)^2}{25} + \frac{(x-1)^2}{9} = 1$$

*State whether the graph of each equation is a circle, parabola, or ellipse. Justify your answer.*

6. $x^2 + 4y^2 - 2x - 16y + 1 = 0$

ellipse; $\frac{(x-1)^2}{16} + \frac{(y-2)^2}{4} = 1$

7. $x^2 + 4y - 16 = 0$

parabola; $x^2 = 4(-1)(y - 4)$

8. $x^2 + y^2 + 6x + 2y + 7 = 0$

circle; $(x + 3)^2 + (y + 1)^2 = 3$

9. $4x^2 + 4y^2 - 20x - 24 = 0$

circle; $\left(x - \frac{5}{2}\right)^2 + y^2 = \frac{49}{4}$

Glencoe Division, Macmillan/McGraw-Hill

## 10-4 | Practice Worksheet

### The hyperbola

*Find the coordinates of the center, the foci, and the vertices and the equations of the asymptotes of the graph of each equation. Then graph the equation.*

**1.** $4x^2 - y^2 - 8x + 20 = 0$

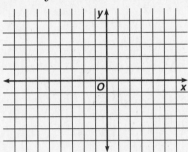

**2.** $x^2 - 4y^2 - 4x + 24y - 36 = 0$

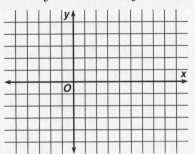

*State whether the graph of each equation is a circle, ellipse, parabola, or hyperbola.*

**3.** $2x^2 + 3y^2 - 6 = 0$

**4.** $25x^2 - 9y^2 + 100x - 54y - 206 = 0$

*Graph each equation.*

**5.** $\dfrac{(x-1)^2}{4} - \dfrac{(y+2)^2}{9} = 1$

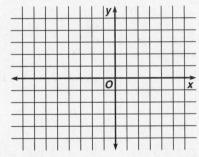

**6.** $xy = -1$

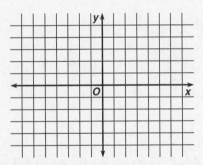

*Write the equation of the hyperbola that meets each set of conditions.*

**7.** The length of the conjugate axis is 6 units, and the vertices are at (–3, 0) and (5, 0).

**8.** The vertices are at (2, 1) and (2, 7), and focus is at (2, 8).

## 10-4 | Practice Worksheet

### The hyperbola

**Find the coordinates of the center, the foci, and the vertices and the equations of the asymptotes of the graph of each equation. Then graph the equation.**

**1.** $4x^2 - y^2 - 8x + 20 = 0$

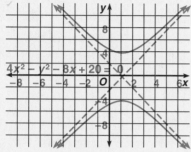

center: (1, 0);
foci: (1, $\pm 2\sqrt{5}$);
vertices: (1, $\pm 4$);
asymptotes: $y = \pm 2(x - 1)$

**2.** $x^2 - 4y^2 - 4x + 24y - 36 = 0$

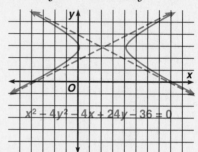

center: (2, 3);
foci: ($2 \pm \sqrt{5}$, 3);
vertices: (0, 3), (4, 3);
asymptotes: $y - 3 = \pm \dfrac{1}{2}(x - 2)$

**State whether the graph of each equation is a circle, ellipse, parabola, or hyperbola.**

**3.** $2x^2 + 3y^2 - 6 = 0$
ellipse

**4.** $25x^2 - 9y^2 + 100x - 54y - 206 = 0$
hyperbola

**Graph each equation.**

**5.** $\dfrac{(x-1)^2}{4} - \dfrac{(y+2)^2}{9} = 1$

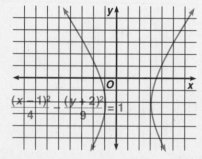

**6.** $xy = -1$

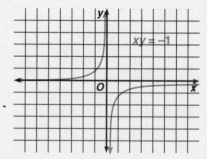

**Write the equation of the hyperbola that meets each set of conditions.**

**7.** The length of the conjugate axis is 6 units, and the vertices are at (−3, 0) and (5, 0).

$$\dfrac{(x-1)^2}{16} - \dfrac{y^2}{9} = 1$$

**8.** The vertices are at (2, 1) and (2, 7), and focus is at (2, 8).

$$\dfrac{(y-4)^2}{9} - \dfrac{(x-2)^2}{7} = 1$$

# 10-5 Practice Worksheet

## Conic Sections

**Determine the eccentricity of the conic section represented by each equation.**

**1.** $4x^2 + 9y^2 + 54y + 45 = 0$

**2.** $(y + 1)^2 = 3(x + 4)$

**Identify the conic section represented by each equation. Write the equation in standard form and graph the equation.**

**3.** $x^2 - 4y = -4$

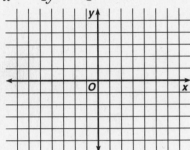

**4.** $x^2 + y^2 - 6x - 6y = 18$

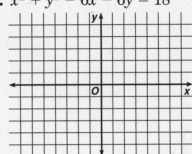

**5.** $4x^2 - y^2 - 8x + 6y = 9$

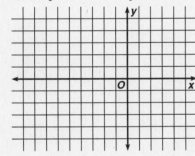

**6.** $9x^2 + 5y^2 + 18x = 36$

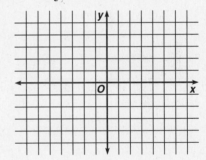

**Write the equation of the conic that meets each set of conditions.**

**7.** a hyperbola with a vertical transverse axis 10 units long, center at $(2, 0)$, and $e = 2$

**8.** an ellipse with center at $(2, -2)$, a vertical semi-major axis 4 units long, and $e = 0.5$

**10-5** **Practice Worksheet**

## Conic Sections

**Determine the eccentricity of the conic section represented by each equation.**

**1.** $4x^2 + 9y^2 + 54y + 45 = 0$

$$\frac{\sqrt{5}}{3}$$

**2.** $(y + 1)^2 = 3(x + 4)$

**1**

**Identify the conic section represented by each equation. Write the equation in standard form and graph the equation.**

**3.** $x^2 - 4y = -4$

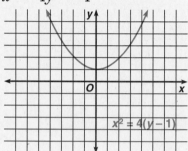

parabola; $x^2 = 4(y - 1)$

**4.** $x^2 + y^2 - 6x - 6y = 18$

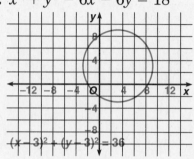

circle; $(x - 3)^2 + (y - 3)^2 = 36$

**5.** $4x^2 - y^2 - 8x + 6y = 9$

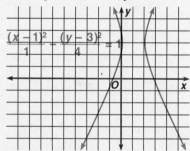

hyperbola; $\dfrac{(x - 1)^2}{1} - \dfrac{(y - 3)^2}{4} = 1$

**6.** $9x^2 + 5y^2 + 18x = 36$

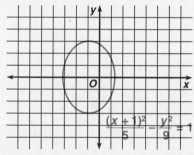

ellipse; $\dfrac{(x + 1)^2}{5} + \dfrac{y^2}{9} = 1$

**Write the equation of the conic that meets each set of conditions.**

**7.** a hyperbola with a vertical transverse axis 10 units long, center at (2, 0), and $e = 2$

$$\frac{y^2}{25} - \frac{(x - 2)^2}{75} = 1$$

**8.** an ellipse with center at (2, –2), a vertical semi-major axis 4 units long, and $e = 0.5$

$$\frac{(y + 2)^2}{16} + \frac{(x - 2)^2}{12} = 1$$

Glencoe Division, Macmillan/McGraw-Hill

# 10-6 Practice Worksheet

## Transformations of Conics

**Identify the graph of each equation. Write the equation of the translated graph in general form. Then draw the graph.**

**1.** $x^2 + y^2 = 9$ for $T_{(-2, 1)}$

**2.** $2x^2 - 4x + 3 - y = 0$ for $T_{(1, -1)}$

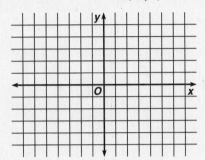

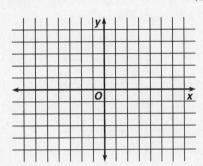

**Suppose the graph of each equation is rotated about the origin for the given angle. Find an equation of the rotated graph.**

**3.** $x^2 - y^2 = 16$, $\theta = 45°$

**4.** $21x^2 - 10\sqrt{3}xy + 31y^2 = 144$, $\theta = 30°$

**Identify the graph of each equation. Then find $\theta$ to the nearest degree.**

**5.** $2x^2 - 4xy + y^2 + 3 = 0$

**6.** $x^2 + 3xy + 3y^2 = 3$

**7.** $3x^2 + 4\sqrt{3}xy - y^2 = 15$

Glencoe Division, Macmillan/McGraw-Hill

**10-6** | # Practice Worksheet

## Transformations of Conics

*Identify the graph of each equation. Write the equation of the translated graph in general form. Then draw the graph.*

**1.** $x^2 + y^2 = 9$ for $T_{(-2, 1)}$

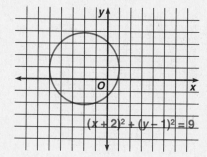

$(x+2)^2 + (y-1)^2 = 9$

**2.** $2x^2 - 4x + 3 - y = 0$ for $T_{(1, -1)}$

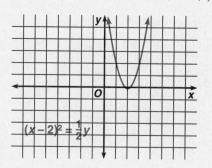

$(x-2)^2 = \frac{1}{2}y$

**circle; $(x + 2)^2 + (y - 1)^2 = 9$**

**parabola; $(x - 2)^2 = 4\left(\dfrac{1}{8}\right)(y - 0)$**

*Suppose the graph of each equation is rotated about the origin for the given angle. Find an equation of the rotated graph.*

**3.** $x^2 - y^2 = 16$, $\theta = 45°$

**$xy = 8$**

**4.** $21x^2 - 10\sqrt{3}xy + 31y^2 = 144$, $\theta = 30°$

**$\dfrac{x^2}{9} + \dfrac{y^2}{4} = 1$**

*Identify the graph of each equation. Then find $\theta$ to the nearest degree.*

**5.** $2x^2 - 4xy + y^2 + 3 = 0$
**ellipse; 38°**

**6.** $x^2 + 3xy + 3y^2 = 3$
**hyperbola; 45°**

**7.** $3x^2 + 4\sqrt{3}xy - y^2 = 15$
**hyperbola; 30°**

Glencoe Division, Macmillan/McGraw-Hill

# 10-7 Practice Worksheet

## Systems of Second-Degree Equations and Inequalities.

*Graph each system of equations. Then solve. Round the coordinates of the solutions to the nearest tenth.*

**1.** $2x - y = 8$
$x^2 + y^2 = 9$

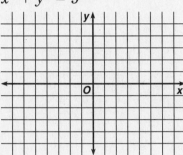

**2.** $x^2 - y^2 = 4$
$y = 1$

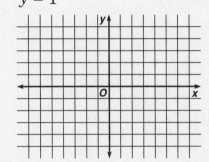

**3.** $xy = 4$
$x^2 = y^2 + 1$

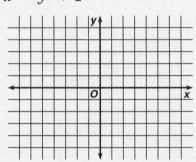

**4.** $x^2 + y^2 = 4$
$4x^2 + 9y^2 = 36$

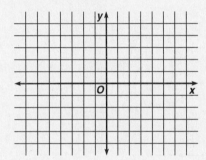

## Graph each system of inequalities.

**5.** $3 \geq (y - 1)^2 + 2x$
$y \geq -3x + 1$

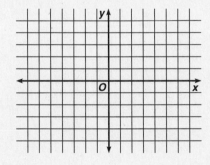

**6.** $(x - 1)^2 + (y - 1)^2 < 4$
$8y^2 + x^2 \leq 16$

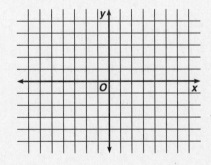

Glencoe Division, Macmillan/McGraw-Hill

**10-7** # Practice Worksheet

## Systems of Second-Degree Equations and Inequalities.

*Graph each system of equations. Then solve. Round the coordinates of the solutions to the nearest tenth.*

**1.** $2x - y = 8$
   $x^2 + y^2 = 9$

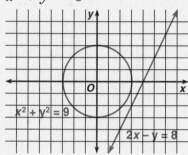

**no real solutions**

**2.** $x^2 - y^2 = 4$
   $y = 1$

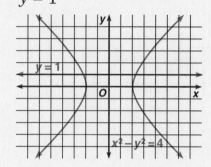

**(−2.2, 1) and (2.2, 1)**

**3.** $xy = 4$
   $x^2 = y^2 + 1$

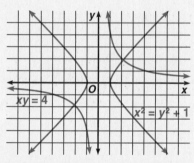

**(2.1, 1.9) and (−2.1, −1.9)**

**4.** $x^2 + y^2 = 4$
   $4x^2 + 9y^2 = 36$

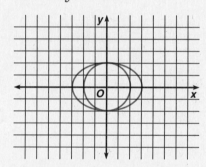

**(0, −2) and (0, 2)**

*Graph each system of inequalities.*

**5.** $3 \geq (y - 1)^2 + 2x$
   $y \geq -3x + 1$

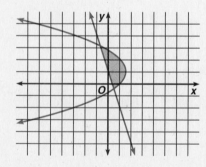

**6.** $(x - 1)^2 + (y - 1)^2 < 4$
   $8y^2 + x^2 \leq 16$

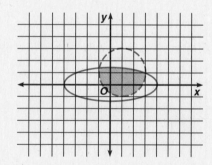

Glencoe Division, Macmillan/McGraw-Hill

# 10-8 Practice Worksheet

## Tangents and Normals to the Conic Sections

*Find the equations of the tangent and the normal to the graphs of each equation at the point with the given coordinates. Write the equations in standard form.*

**1.** $x^2 - 5 = 2 - y^2$, $(1, \sqrt{6})$

**2.** $2x^2 + 4x + 2y = 10$, $(1, 3)$

**3.** $2(x - 1)^2 + y^2 = 10$, $(2, 2\sqrt{2})$

**4.** $2x^2 + 2y^2 = 10$, $(1, 2)$

**5.** $9(x + 1)^2 + 16(y + 3)^2 = 144$, $(-1, 0)$

**6.** $y^2 - x^2 - 6x = 25$, $(0, 5)$

*Find the length of the tangent segment from each point to the graph of the given circle.*

**7.** $(6, 2)$, $x^2 + y^2 = 13$

**8.** $(5, 2)$, $3(x + 1)^2 + 3(y + 1)^2 = 27$

**9.** Find the equations of the horizontal lines tangent to the graph of $x^2 + y^2 = 81$.

**10.** Find the equations of the normals if the lines tangent to the graph of $9x^2 + 4y^2 = 36$ are vertical.

Glencoe Division, Macmillan/McGraw-Hill

**10-8** **Practice Worksheet**

## Tangents and Normals to the Conic Sections

*Find the equations of the tangent and the normal to the graphs of each equation at the point with the given coordinates. Write the equations in standard form.*

**1.** $x^2 - 5 = 2 - y^2$, $(1, \sqrt{6})$
$x \pm \sqrt{6}y - 7 = 0;$
$\sqrt{6}x - y = 0$

**2.** $2x^2 + 4x + 2y = 10$, $(1, 3)$
$4x + y - 6 = 0;$
$x - 4y + 7 = 0$

**3.** $2(x - 1)^2 + y^2 = 10$, $(2, 2\sqrt{2})$
$\sqrt{2}x + 2y - 6\sqrt{2} = 0;$
$\sqrt{2}x - y = 0$

**4.** $2x^2 + 2y^2 = 10$, $(1, 2)$
$x + 2y - 5 = 0;$
$2x - y = 0$

**5.** $9(x + 1)^2 + 16(y + 3)^2 = 144$, $(-1, 0)$
$y = 0;\ x = -1$

**6.** $y^2 - x^2 - 6x = 25$, $(0, 5)$
$3x - 5y + 25 = 0;$
$5x + 3y - 15 = 0$

*Find the length of the tangent segment from each point to the graph of the given circle.*

**7.** $(6, 2)$, $x^2 + y^2 = 13$
$3\sqrt{3}$

**8.** $(5, 2)$, $3(x + 1)^2 + 3(y + 1)^2 = 27$
$6$

**9.** Find the equations of the horizontal lines tangent to the graph of $x^2 + y^2 = 81$.
$y = \pm 9$

**10.** Find the equations of the normals if the lines tangent to the graph of $9x^2 + 4y^2 = 36$ are vertical.
$y = 0$

Glencoe Division, Macmillan/McGraw-Hill

## 11-1 Practice Worksheet

### Rational Exponents

**Evaluate.**

1. $\sqrt[3]{216}$

2. $2^{-5} \cdot 2^7$

3. $\sqrt[3]{8^3}$

4. $\left(4^{\frac{7}{3}}\right)^3$

5. $\left(144^{\frac{1}{2}}\right)^3$

6. $\left(12^{-\frac{2}{3}}\right)^{\frac{3}{2}}$

**Express using rational exponents.**

7. $\sqrt{x^5 y^6}$

8. $\sqrt[3]{c^7}$

9. $\sqrt{144 x^6 y^{10}}$

10. $\sqrt[5]{27 x^{10} y^5}$

11. $\sqrt{1024 a^3}$

12. $\sqrt[4]{36 a^8 b^5}$

**Express using radicals.**

13. $64^{\frac{1}{3}}$

14. $y^{\frac{3}{2}}$

15. $2^{\frac{1}{2}} a^{\frac{3}{2}} b^{\frac{5}{2}}$

16. $x^{\frac{2}{5}} y^{\frac{3}{5}}$

17. $(s^2 t)^{\frac{1}{3}} v^{\frac{2}{3}}$

18. $(x^6 y^3)^{\frac{1}{2}} z^{\frac{3}{2}}$

**Simplify.**

19. $(x^{-2})^3 \cdot (x^3)^{-2}$

20. $(3y^3)(3y)^3$

21. $x^7 \cdot x^5 \cdot x^{-7} \cdot x^{-5}$

Glencoe Division, Macmillan/McGraw-Hill

**11-1** # Practice Worksheet

## Rational Exponents

*Evaluate.*

1. $\sqrt[3]{216}$
   **6**

2. $2^{-5} \cdot 2^7$
   **4**

3. $\sqrt[3]{8^3}$
   **8**

4. $\left(4^{\frac{7}{3}}\right)^3$
   **16,384**

5. $\left(144^{\frac{1}{2}}\right)^3$
   **1728**

6. $\left(12^{-\frac{2}{3}}\right)^{\frac{3}{2}}$
   $\dfrac{1}{12}$

*Express using rational exponents.*

7. $\sqrt{x^5 y^6}$
   $x^{\frac{5}{2}} y^3$

8. $\sqrt[3]{c^7}$
   $c^{\frac{7}{3}}$

9. $\sqrt{144 x^6 y^{10}}$
   $12 x^3 y^5$

10. $\sqrt[5]{27 x^{10} y^5}$
    $27^{\frac{1}{5}} x^2 y$

11. $\sqrt{1024 a^3}$
    $32 a^{\frac{3}{2}}$

12. $\sqrt[4]{36 a^8 b^5}$
    $6^{\frac{1}{2}} a^2 b^{\frac{5}{4}}$

*Express using radicals.*

13. $64^{\frac{1}{3}}$

    $\sqrt[3]{64}$ *or* 4

14. $y^{\frac{3}{2}}$

    $\sqrt{y^3}$

15. $2^{\frac{1}{2}} a^{\frac{3}{2}} b^{\frac{5}{2}}$

    $\sqrt{2 a^3 b^5}$

16. $x^{\frac{2}{5}} y^{\frac{3}{5}}$

    $\sqrt[5]{x^2 y^3}$

17. $(s^2 t)^{\frac{1}{3}} v^{\frac{2}{3}}$

    $\sqrt[3]{s^2 t v^2}$

18. $(x^6 y^3)^{\frac{1}{2}} z^{\frac{3}{2}}$

    $\sqrt{x^6 y^3 z^3}$

*Simplify.*

19. $(x^{-2})^3 \cdot (x^3)^{-2}$
    $x^{-12}$

20. $(3y^3)(3y)^3$
    $81 y^6$

21. $x^7 \cdot x^5 \cdot x^{-7} \cdot x^{-5}$
    **1**

Glencoe Division, Macmillan/McGraw-Hill

# 11-2 Practice Worksheet

## Exponential Functions

*Use a calculator to evaluate each expression to the nearest ten thousandth.*

**1.** $3^{\sqrt{2}}$             **2.** $4^{\sqrt{2}}$             **3.** $5^{\sqrt{6}}$

*Graph each equation.*

**4.** $y = 2^{x-1}$

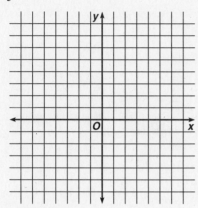

**5.** $y = 3^{x-2}$

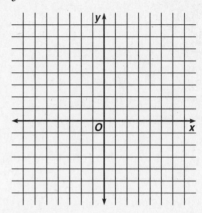

**6.** $y = -2^{x+1}$

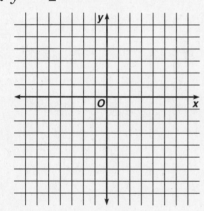

**7.** $y = 2^{-x-1}$

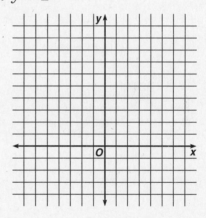

*Graph each inequality.*

**8.** $y > 2^{x}$

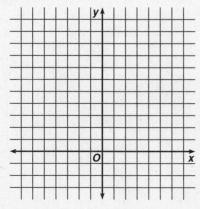

**9.** $y \geq (0.5)^{x}$

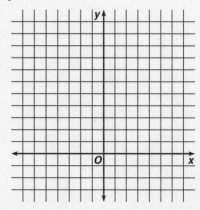

Glencoe Division, Macmillan/McGraw-Hill

# 11-2 **Practice Worksheet**

## *Exponential Functions*

**Use a calculator to evaluate each expression to the nearest ten thousandth.**

**1.** $3^{\sqrt{2}}$

**2.** $4^{\sqrt{2}}$

**3.** $5^{\sqrt{6}}$

**Graph each equation.**

**4.** $y = 2^{x-1}$

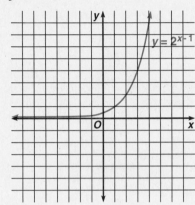

**5.** $y = 3^{x-2}$

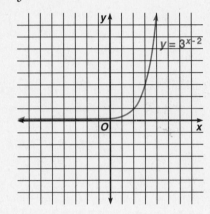

**6.** $y = -2^{x+1}$

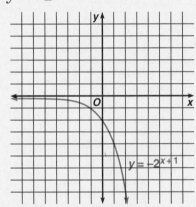

**7.** $y = 2^{-x-1}$

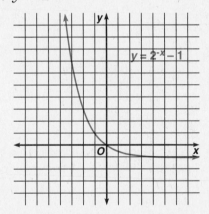

**Graph each inequality.**

**8.** $y > 2^x$

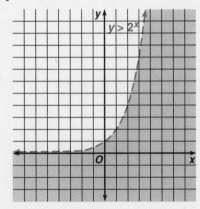

**9.** $y \geq (0.5)^x$

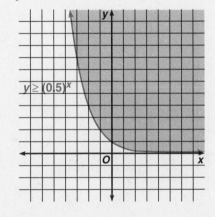

Glencoe Division, Macmillan/McGraw-Hill

**11-3** **Practice Worksheet**

## The Number e

*Use a calculator to evaluate each expression to the nearest ten thousandth.*

**1.** $e^{2.3}$

**2.** $e^{4.6}$

**3.** $\sqrt{e}$

**4.** $2\sqrt[3]{e^4}$

**5.** $3\sqrt{e^3}$

**6.** $e^{-2}$

*Use a graphing calculator to graph each equation. Sketch the graph below. Then determine the interval in which each function is increasing or decreasing.*

**7.** $y = 2e^x + 1$

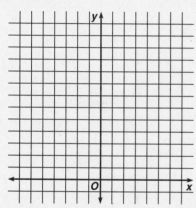

**8.** $y = -3e^x$

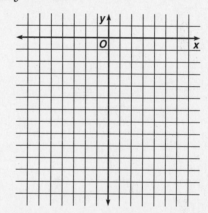

*Given the original principal, the annual interest rate, and the amount of time for each investment, and the type of compounded interest, find the amount at the end of the investment.*

**9.** $P = \$1250$, $r = 8.5\%$, $t = 3$ years, quarterly

**10.** $P = \$2575$, $r = 6.25\%$, $t = 5$ years 3 months, continuously

**11-3** **Practice Worksheet**

## The Number e

*Use a calculator to evaluate each expression to the nearest ten thousandth.*

**1.** $e^{2.3}$
    **9.9742**

**2.** $e^{4.6}$
    **99.4843**

**3.** $\sqrt{e}$
    **1.6487**

**4.** $2\sqrt[3]{e^4}$
    **7.5873**

**5.** $3\sqrt{e^3}$
    **13.4451**

**6.** $e^{-2}$
    **0.1353**

*Use a graphing calculator to graph each equation. Sketch the graph below. Then determine the interval in which each function is increasing or decreasing.*

**7.** $y = 2e^x + 1$

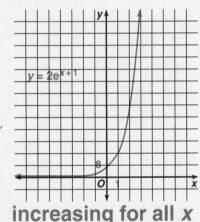

**increasing for all *x***

**8.** $y = -3e^x$

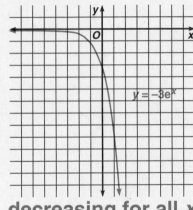

**decreasing for all *x***

*Given the original principal, the annual interest rate, and the amount of time for each investment, and the type of compounded interest, find the amount at the end of the investment.*

**9.** $P = \$1250$, $r = 8.5\%$, $t = 3$ years, quarterly
    **$1608.77**

**10.** $P = \$2575$, $r = 6.25\%$, $t = 5$ years 3 months, continuously
    **$3575.03**

Glencoe Division, Macmillan/McGraw-Hill

# Practice Worksheet

## Logarithmic Functions

**Write each equation in logarithmic form.**

**1.** $2^5 = 32$

**2.** $5^{-3} = \frac{1}{125}$

**3.** $6^{-3} = \frac{1}{216}$

**Write each equation in exponential form.**

**4.** $\log_3 27 = 3$

**5.** $\log_4 16 = 2$

**6.** $\log_{10} \frac{1}{100} = -2$

**Evaluate each expression.**

**7.** $\log_7 7^3$

**8.** $\log_{10} 0.001$

**9.** $3^{\log_3 6}$

**10.** $\log_b b^{-4}$

**11.** $\log_a a$

**12.** $3^{4 \log_3 4}$

**Solve each equation.**

**13.** $\log_x 64 = 3$

**14.** $\log_4 0.25 = x$

**15.** $\log_4 (2x - 1) = \log_4 16$

**16.** $\log_{10} \sqrt{10} = x$

**Graph each equation or inequality.**

**17.** $y = \log_2 x$

**18.** $y < \log_{10} (x - 1)$

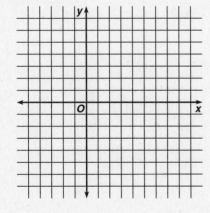

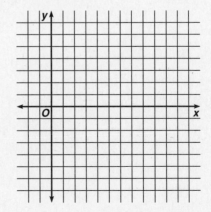

## 11-4 **Practice Worksheet**

### *Logarithmic Functions*

**Write each equation in logarithmic form.**

**1.** $2^5 = 32$

$$\log_2 32 = 5$$

**2.** $5^{-3} = \frac{1}{125}$

$$\log_5 \frac{1}{125} = -3$$

**3.** $6^{-3} = \frac{1}{216}$

$$\log_6 \frac{1}{216} = -3$$

**Write each equation in exponential form.**

**4.** $\log_3 27 = 3$

$$3^3 = 27$$

**5.** $\log_4 16 = 2$

$$4^2 = 16$$

**6.** $\log_{10} \frac{1}{100} = -2$

$$10^{-2} = \frac{1}{100}$$

**Evaluate each expression.**

**7.** $\log_7 7^3$
**3**

**8.** $\log_{10} 0.001$
**−3**

**9.** $3^{\log_3 6}$
**6**

**10.** $\log_b b^{-4}$
**−4**

**11.** $\log_a a$
**1**

**12.** $3^{4 \log_3 4}$
**256**

**Solve each equation.**

**13.** $\log_x 64 = 3$
**4**

**14.** $\log_4 0.25 = x$
**−1**

**15.** $\log_4 (2x - 1) = \log_4 16$
$$\frac{17}{2}$$

**16.** $\log_{10} \sqrt{10} = x$
$$\frac{1}{2}$$

**Graph each equation or inequality.**

**17.** $y = \log_2 x$

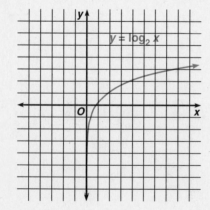

**18.** $y < \log_{10} (x - 1)$

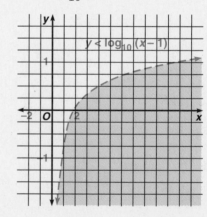

Glencoe Division, Macmillan/McGraw-Hill

# 11-5 | Practice Worksheet

## Common Logarithms

*Use a calculator to find the common logarithm of each number to the nearest ten thousandth.*

**1.** 726.5

**2.** 0.6351

**3.** 0.0026

**4.** 0.852

**5.** 16,256

**6.** $3.2 \times 10^4$

*Use a calculator to find the antilogarithm of each number to the nearest hundredth.*

**7.** 0.6259

**8.** 2.7356

**9.** −0.0251

**10.** −1.2619

**11.** 4.3251

**12.** 2.6359 −3

*Evaluate each expression by using logarithms. Check your work with a calculator.*

**13.** $261 \times 32 \times 0.32$

**14.** $\frac{181.72 \times 7.01}{4.62}$

**15.** $2.43 \times (8.9)^4$

**16.** $\sqrt{2.69 \times 4.180}$

**17.** $\sqrt[3]{(2.69)(420)}$

**18.** $16.21 \div \sqrt[4]{4.29}$

Glencoe Division, Macmillan/McGraw-Hill

# 11-5 Practice Worksheet

## Common Logarithms

*Use a calculator to find the common logarithm of each number to the nearest ten thousandth.*

**1.** 726.5
**2.8612**

**2.** 0.6351
**−0.1972**

**3.** 0.0026
**−2.5850**

**4.** 0.852
**−0.0696**

**5.** 16,256
**4.2110**

**6.** $3.2 \times 10^4$
**4.5051**

*Use a calculator to find the antilogarithm of each number to the nearest hundredth.*

**7.** 0.6259
**423**

**8.** 2.7356
**544.00**

**9.** −0.0251
**0.94**

**10.** −1.2619
**0.05**

**11.** 4.3251
**21,139.76**

**12.** 2.6359 −3
**0.43**

*Evaluate each expression by using logarithms. Check your work with a calculator.*

**13.** $261 \times 32 \times 0.32$

**2672.64**

**14.** $\frac{181.72 \times 7.01}{4.62}$

**275.73**

**15.** $2.43 \times (8.9)^4$
**15,246.36**

**16.** $\sqrt{2.69 \times 4.180}$
**3.35**

**17.** $\sqrt[3]{(2.69)(420)}$
**10.42**

**18.** $16.21 \div \sqrt[4]{4.29}$
**11.26**

Glencoe Division, Macmillan/McGraw-Hill

# 11-6 Practice Worksheet

## Exponential and Logarithmic Equations

*Solve each equation or inequality by using logarithms.*

**1.** $8^x = 10$

**2.** $12^x = 18$

**3.** $2.4^x \leq 20$

**4.** $1.8^{x-5} = 19.8$

**5.** $4^{2x+1} = 15.2$

**6.** $3^{5x} = 85$

**7.** $x < \log_2 15$

**8.** $x \geq \log_3 12.3$

**9.** $x^{\frac{2}{3}} > 25.3$

**10.** $x^{0.4} = 18.9$

**11.** $3^{2x-2} = 2x$

**12.** $4^{1-2x} = 3^{2x}$

Glencoe Division, Macmillan/McGraw-Hill

# 11-6 Practice Worksheet

## Exponential and Logarithmic Equations

*Solve each equation or inequality by using logarithms.*

**1.** $8^x = 10$
**1.1073**

**2.** $12^x = 18$
**1.1632**

**3.** $2.4^x \leq 20$
$x \leq$ **3.4219**

**4.** $1.8^{x-5} = 19.8$
**10.0795**

**5.** $4^{2x+1} = 15.2$
**0.4815**

**6.** $3^{5x} = 85$
**0.8088**

**7.** $x < \log_2 15$
$x <$ **3.9069**

**8.** $x \geq \log_3 12.3$
$x \geq$ **2.2843**

**9.** $x^{\frac{2}{3}} > 25.3$
$x \geq$ **127.2567**

**10.** $x^{0.4} = 18.9$
**1552.9394**

**11.** $3^{2x-2} = 2x$
**1.4608**

**12.** $4^{1-2x} = 3^{2x}$
**0.2789**

Glencoe Division, Macmillan/McGraw-Hill

**11-7**

# Practice Worksheet

## Natural Logarithms

*Use a calculator to find each value to the nearest ten thousandth.*

**1.** ln 43.2

**2.** ln 0.0217

**3.** ln 985

**4.** ln 0.0076

**5.** ln 10

**6.** ln $\frac{1}{0.6}$

**7.** antiln (–0.256)

**8.** antiln 4.62

**9.** antiln (–1.62)

*Solve each equation.*

**10.** $1500 = 6e^{0.043t}$

**11.** $1249 = 175e^{-0.04t}$

**12.** $\ln 6.7 = \ln (e^{0.21t})$

**13.** $\ln 724.6 = \ln (e^{6.3t})$

**14. Banking**  Ms. Cubbatz invested a sum of money in a certificate of deposit that pays 8% interest compounded continuously. Recall that the formula for the amount in an account earning interest compounded continuously is $A = Pe^{rt}$. If Ms. Cubbatz made the investment on January 1, 1989 and the account is worth $12,000 on January 1, 1993, what was the original amount in the account?

# 11-7 Practice Worksheet

## Natural Logarithms

*Use a calculator to find each value to the nearest ten thousandth.*

**1.** ln 43.2
**3.7658**

**2.** ln 0.0217
**−3.8304**

**3.** ln 985
**6.8926**

**4.** ln 0.0076
**−4.8796**

**5.** ln 10
**2.3026**

**6.** ln $\frac{1}{0.6}$
**0.5108**

**7.** antiln (−0.256)
**0.7741**

**8.** antiln 4.62
**101.4940**

**9.** antiln (−1.62)
**0.1979**

*Solve each equation.*

**10.** $1500 = 6e^{0.043t}$
**128.41**

**11.** $1249 = 175e^{-0.04t}$
**−49.13**

**12.** $\ln 6.7 = \ln (e^{0.21t})$
**9.06**

**13.** $\ln 724.6 = \ln (e^{6.3t})$
**1.05**

**14. Banking**   Ms. Cubbatz invested a sum of money in a certificate of deposit that pays 8% interest compounded continuously. Recall that the formula for the amount in an account earning interest compounded continuously is $A = Pe^{rt}$. If Ms. Cubbatz made the investment on January 1, 1989 and the account is worth $12,000 on January 1, 1993, what was the original amount in the account?
**$8713.79**

# 12-1 Practice Worksheet

## Arithmetic Sequences and Series

*Solve.*

1. Find the 24th term in the sequence for which $a = -27$ and $d = 3$.

2. Find $n$ for the sequence for which $a_n = 27$, $a = -12$, and $d = 3$.

3. Find $d$ for the sequence for which $a = -12$ and $a_{23} = 32$.

4. Find the first term in the sequence for which $d = -3$ and $a_6 = 5$.

5. Find the first term in the sequence for which $a_4 = -21$ and $a_7 = -3$.

6. Find the sixth term in the sequence $-3 + \sqrt{2},\ 0,\ 3 - \sqrt{2},\ \cdots$.

7. Find the 45th term in the sequence $-17, -11, -5, \cdots$.

8. Form a sequence that has one arithmetic mean between 35 and 45.

9. Find the sum of the first 13 terms in the series
   $-5 + 1 + 7 + \cdots + 43$.

Glencoe Division, Macmillan/McGraw-Hill

**12-1** **Practice Worksheet**

## Arithmetic Sequences and Series

*Solve.*

1. Find the 24th term in the sequence for which $a = -27$ and $d = 3$.

   **42**

2. Find $n$ for the sequence for which $a_n = 27$, $a = -12$, and $d = 3$.

   **13**

3. Find $d$ for the sequence for which $a = -12$ and $a_{23} = 32$.

   **2**

4. Find the first term in the sequence for which $d = -3$ and $a_6 = 5$.

   **20**

5. Find the first term in the sequence for which $a_4 = -21$ and $a_7 = -3$.

   **−39**

6. Find the sixth term in the sequence $-3 + \sqrt{2}, 0, 3 - \sqrt{2}, \cdots$.

   **12 - 4$\sqrt{2}$**

7. Find the 45th term in the sequence $-17, -11, -5, \cdots$.

   **247**

8. Form a sequence that has one arithmetic mean between 35 and 45.

   **35, 40, 45, . . .**

9. Find the sum of the first 13 terms in the series
   $-5 + 1 + 7 + \cdots + 43$.

   **403**

Glencoe Division, Macmillan/McGraw-Hill

## 12-2 Practice Worksheet

### Geometric Sequences and Series

*Solve.*

1. The first term of a geometric sequence is –4, and the common ratio is $\frac{3}{4}$. Find the next four terms.

2. The first term of a geometric sequence is 12, and the common ratio is $-\frac{3}{2}$. Find the next four terms.

3. Find the ninth term of the geometric sequence $\sqrt{3}, -3, 3\sqrt{3}, \cdots$.

4. Find the fifth term of the geometric sequence $20, 0.2, 0.002, \cdots$.

5. Find the first term of the geometric sequence for which $a_5 = 64\sqrt{2}$ and $r = \sqrt{2}$.

6. Find the first three terms of the geometric sequence for which $a_4 = 8.4$ and $r = 4$.

7. Form a sequence that has one geometric mean between $\frac{1}{9}$ and 3.

8. Find the sum of the first eight terms of the series $\frac{3}{4} + \frac{9}{20} + \frac{27}{100} + \cdots$.

Glencoe Division, Macmillan/McGraw-Hill

# 12-2 Practice Worksheet

## Geometric Sequences and Series

*Solve.*

1. The first term of a geometric sequence is –4, and the common ratio is $\frac{3}{4}$. Find the next four terms.

   $-3, -\dfrac{9}{4}, -\dfrac{27}{16}, -\dfrac{81}{64}$

2. The first term of a geometric sequence is 12, and the common ratio is $-\frac{3}{2}$. Find the next four terms.

   $-18, 27, -\dfrac{81}{2}, \dfrac{243}{4}$

3. Find the ninth term of the geometric sequence $\sqrt{3}, -3, 3\sqrt{3}, \cdots$.

   $81\sqrt{3}$

4. Find the fifth term of the geometric sequence $20, 0.2, 0.002, \cdots$.

   $0.0000002$

5. Find the first term of the geometric sequence for which $a_5 = 64\sqrt{2}$ and $r = \sqrt{2}$.

   $16\sqrt{2}$

6. Find the first three terms of the geometric sequence for which $a_4 = 8.4$ and $r = 4$.

   $0.13125, 0.525, 2.1$

7. Form a sequence that has one geometric mean between $\frac{1}{9}$ and 3.

   $\dfrac{1}{9}, \dfrac{\sqrt{3}}{3}, 3$ or $\dfrac{1}{9}, -\dfrac{\sqrt{3}}{3}, 3$

8. Find the sum of the first eight terms of the series $\frac{3}{4} + \frac{9}{20} + \frac{27}{100} + \cdots$.

   $1.84351$

# 12-3 Practice Worksheet

## Infinite Sequences and Series

**Evaluate each limit, or state that the limit does not exist.**

1. $\lim\limits_{n\to\infty} \dfrac{n^2-1}{n^2+1}$

2. $\lim\limits_{n\to\infty} \dfrac{4n^2-5n}{3n^2+4}$

3. $\lim\limits_{n\to\infty} \dfrac{5n^2+1}{6n}$

4. $\lim\limits_{n\to\infty} \dfrac{(n-1)(3n+1)}{5n^2}$

5. $\lim\limits_{n\to\infty} \dfrac{5n^3+1}{3n^2+1}$

6. $\lim\limits_{n\to\infty} \dfrac{3n-(-1)^n}{4n^2}$

**Write each repeating decimal as a fraction.**

7. $0.49999\cdots$

8. $1.999\cdots$

9. $2.242424\cdots$

10. $0.127127\cdots$

11. $1.164164\cdots$

12. $0.6414141\cdots$

**Find the sum of each infinite series, or state that the sum does not exist.**

13. $\dfrac{2}{5} + \dfrac{6}{25} + \dfrac{18}{125}\cdots$

14. $\dfrac{3}{4} + \dfrac{15}{8} + \dfrac{75}{16} + \ldots$

Glencoe Division, Macmillan/McGraw-Hill

# Practice Worksheet

## Infinite Sequences and Series

**Evaluate each limit, or state that the limit does not exist.**

**1.** $\lim\limits_{n \to \infty} \dfrac{n^2 - 1}{n^2 + 1}$

1

**2.** $\lim\limits_{n \to \infty} \dfrac{4n^2 - 5n}{3n^2 + 4}$

$\dfrac{4}{3}$

**3.** $\lim\limits_{n \to \infty} \dfrac{5n^2 + 1}{6n}$

**does not exist**

**4.** $\lim\limits_{n \to \infty} \dfrac{(n-1)(3n+1)}{5n^2}$

$\dfrac{3}{5}$

**5.** $\lim\limits_{n \to \infty} \dfrac{5n^3 + 1}{3n^2 + 1}$

**does not exist**

**6.** $\lim\limits_{n \to \infty} \dfrac{3n - (-1)^n}{4n^2}$

0

**Write each repeating decimal as a fraction.**

**7.** $0.49999 \cdots$

$\dfrac{1}{2}$

**8.** $1.999 \cdots$

2

**9.** $2.242424 \cdots$

$2\dfrac{8}{33}$

**10.** $0.127127 \cdots$

$\dfrac{127}{999}$

**11.** $1.164164 \cdots$

$1\dfrac{164}{999}$

**12.** $0.6414141 \cdots$

$\dfrac{127}{198}$

**Find the sum of each infinite series, or state that the sum does not exist.**

**13.** $\dfrac{2}{5} + \dfrac{6}{25} + \dfrac{18}{125} \cdots$

1

**14.** $\dfrac{3}{4} + \dfrac{15}{8} + \dfrac{75}{16} + \cdots$

**does not exist**

Glencoe Division, Macmillan/McGraw-Hill

**12-4** **Practice Worksheet**

## Convergent and Divergent Series

*Use the ratio test to determine whether each series is convergent or divergent.*

**1.** $1 + \frac{2^2}{2^2} + \frac{3^2}{2^2} + \frac{4^2}{2^2} + \ldots$

**2.** $0.006 + 0.06 + 0.6 + \ldots$

**3.** $\frac{4}{1 \cdot 2 \cdot 3} + \frac{8}{1 \cdot 2 \cdot 3 \cdot 4} + \frac{16}{1 \cdot 2 \cdot 3 \cdot 4 \cdot 5} + \ldots$

**4.** $1 + \frac{1}{3^3} + \frac{1}{5^3} + \frac{1}{7^3} + \ldots$

*Use the comparison test to determine whether each series is convergent or divergent.*

**5.** $1 + \frac{1}{2^3} + \frac{1}{3^3} + \frac{1}{4^3} + \ldots$

**6.** $1 + \frac{1}{2} + \frac{4}{3} + \frac{9}{4} + \ldots$

Glencoe Division, Macmillan/McGraw-Hill

## 12-4 Practice Worksheet

### Convergent and Divergent Series

**Use the ratio test to determine whether each series is convergent or divergent.**

**1.** $1 + \frac{2^2}{2^2} + \frac{3^2}{2^2} + \frac{4^2}{2^2} + \ldots$

**divergent**

**2.** $0.006 + 0.06 + 0.6 + \ldots$

**divergent**

**3.** $\frac{4}{1 \cdot 2 \cdot 3} + \frac{8}{1 \cdot 2 \cdot 3 \cdot 4} + \frac{16}{1 \cdot 2 \cdot 3 \cdot 4 \cdot 5} + \ldots$

**convergent**

**4.** $1 + \frac{1}{3^3} + \frac{1}{5^3} + \frac{1}{7^3} + \ldots$

**convergent**

**Use the comparison test to determine whether each series is convergent or divergent.**

**5.** $1 + \frac{1}{2^3} + \frac{1}{3^3} + \frac{1}{4^3} + \ldots$

**convergent**

**6.** $1 + \frac{1}{2} + \frac{4}{3} + \frac{9}{4} + \ldots$

**divergent**

Glencoe Division, Macmillan/McGraw-Hill

# 12-5 Practice Worksheet

## Sigma Notation and the nth Term

**Evaluate each expression.**

**1.** $7!$

**2.** $3(4!)$

**3.** $6!2!$

**Write each expression in expanded form and find the sum.**

**4.** $\displaystyle\sum_{k=3}^{5} (k^2 - 2^k)$

**5.** $\displaystyle\sum_{q=1}^{4} \frac{2}{q}$

**6.** $\displaystyle\sum_{t=1}^{5} t(t-1)$

**7.** $\displaystyle\sum_{t=0}^{3} (2t-3)$

**8.** $\displaystyle\sum_{c=2}^{5} (c-1)^2$

**9.** $\displaystyle\sum_{i=1}^{\infty} 10\left(\frac{1}{2}\right)^i$

**Express each series using sigma notation.**

**10.** $3 + 6 + 9 + 12 + 15$

**11.** $3 + 9 + 27 + \cdots + 243$

**12.** $\frac{1}{1} + \frac{1}{4} + \frac{1}{9} + \cdots + \frac{1}{100}$

**13.** $24 + 19 + 14 + \cdots + (-1)$

**14.** $\frac{3}{1} + \frac{3}{3} + \frac{3}{5} + \cdots + \frac{3}{67}$

**15.** $\frac{2 \cdot 3}{2} + \frac{3 \cdot 4}{5} + \frac{4 \cdot 5}{10} + \cdots + \frac{6 \cdot 7}{26}$

Glencoe Division, Macmillan/McGraw-Hill

# 12-5 Practice Worksheet

## Sigma Notation and the nth Term

**Evaluate each expression.**

**1.** $7!$

**5040**

**2.** $3(4!)$

**72**

**3.** $6!2!$

**1440**

**Write each expression in expanded form and find the sum.**

**4.** $\displaystyle\sum_{k=3}^{5} (k^2 - 2^k)$

$(3^2 - 2^3) + (4^2 - 2^4) +$
$(5^2 - 2^5); -6$

**5.** $\displaystyle\sum_{q=1}^{4} \frac{2}{q}$

$\dfrac{2}{1} + \dfrac{2}{2} + \dfrac{2}{3} + \dfrac{2}{4};$

$\dfrac{25}{6}$

**6.** $\displaystyle\sum_{t=1}^{5} t(t-1)$

$1(1-1) + 2(2-1) +$
$3(3-1) + 4(4-1) +$
$5(5-1); 40$

**7.** $\displaystyle\sum_{t=0}^{3} (2t-3)$

$(2(0)-3) + (2(1)-3) +$
$(2(2)-3) + (2(3)-3); 0$

**8.** $\displaystyle\sum_{c=2}^{5} (c-1)^2$

$(2-1)^2 + (3-1)^2 +$
$(4-1)^2 + (5-1)^2; 30$

**9.** $\displaystyle\sum_{i=1}^{\infty} 10\left(\frac{1}{2}\right)^i$

$10\left(\dfrac{1}{2}\right)^1 + 10\left(\dfrac{1}{2}\right)^2 +$

$10\left(\dfrac{1}{2}\right)^3 + \cdots; 10$

**Express each series using sigma notation.**

**10.** $3 + 6 + 9 + 12 + 15$

$\displaystyle\sum_{i=1}^{5} 3i$

**11.** $3 + 9 + 27 + \cdots + 243$

$\displaystyle\sum_{i=1}^{5} 3^i$

**12.** $\dfrac{1}{1} + \dfrac{1}{4} + \dfrac{1}{9} + \cdots + \dfrac{1}{100}$

$\displaystyle\sum_{i=1}^{10} \frac{1}{i^2}$

**13.** $24 + 19 + 14 + \cdots + (-1)$

$\displaystyle\sum_{i=0}^{5} (24 - 5i)$

**14.** $\dfrac{3}{1} + \dfrac{3}{3} + \dfrac{3}{5} + \cdots + \dfrac{3}{67}$

$\displaystyle\sum_{i=1}^{34} \frac{3}{2i-1}$

**15.** $\dfrac{2 \cdot 3}{2} + \dfrac{3 \cdot 4}{5} + \dfrac{4 \cdot 5}{10} + \cdots + \dfrac{6 \cdot 7}{26}$

$\displaystyle\sum_{i=1}^{5} \frac{(i+1)(i+2)}{i^2+1}$

Glencoe Division, Macmillan/McGraw-Hill

**12-6** **Practice Worksheet**

## The Binomial Theorem

**Use Pascal's triangle to expand each binomial.**

**1.** $(x - y)^4$

**2.** $(r + 3)^5$

**3.** $(m + 2n)^5$

**4.** $(3a - b)^4$

**Use the binomial theorem to expand each binomial.**

**5.** $(x - 5)^4$

**6.** $(3x + 2y)^4$

**7.** $(a - \sqrt{2})^5$

**8.** $(2x - 3y)^6$

**Find the designated term of each binomial expansion.**

**9.** 4th term of $(2n^2 - 3m)^4$

**10.** 3rd term of $(a - 2\sqrt{3})^6$

# 12-6 Practice Worksheet

## The Binomial Theorem

**Use Pascal's triangle to expand each binomial.**

**1.** $(x - y)^4$

$x^4 - 4x^3y + 6x^2y^2 - 4xy^3 + y^4$

**2.** $(r + 3)^5$

$r^5 - 15r^4 + 90r^3 + 270r^2 + 405r + 243$

**3.** $(m + 2n)^5$

$m^5 + 10m^4n + 40m^3n^2 + 80m^2n^3 + 80mn^4 + 32n^5$

**4.** $(3a - b)^4$

$81a^4 - 108a^3b + 54a^2b^2 - 12ab^3 + b^4$

**Use the binomial theorem to expand each binomial.**

**5.** $(x - 5)^4$

$x^4 - 20x^3 + 150x^2 - 500x + 625$

**6.** $(3x + 2y)^4$

$81x^4 + 216x^3y + 216x^2y^2 + 96xy^3 + 16y^4$

**7.** $(a - \sqrt{2})^5$

$a^5 - 5\sqrt{2}a^4 + 20a^3 - 20\sqrt{2}a^2 + 20a - 4\sqrt{2}$

**8.** $(2x - 3y)^6$

$64x^6 - 576x^5y + 2160x^4y^2 - 4320x^3y^3 + 4860x^2y^4 - 2916xy^5 + 729y^6$

**Find the designated term of each binomial expansion.**

**9.** 4th term of $(2n^2 - 3m)^4$

$-216n^2m^3$

**10.** 3rd term of $(a - 2\sqrt{3})^6$

$180a^4$

Glencoe Division, Macmillan/McGraw-Hill

**12-7**

# Practice Worksheet

## Special Sequences and Series

*Use the first five terms of the exponential series $e^x = 1 + x + \frac{x^2}{2!} + \frac{x^3}{3!} + \frac{x^4}{4!} + \ldots$ and a calculator to approximate each value to the nearest hundredth.*

**1.** $e^{0.5}$

**2.** $e^{1.2}$

**3.** $e^{3.1}$

**4.** $e^{2.7}$

**5.** $e^{0.9}$

**6.** $e^{2.2}$

*Use the first five terms of the appropriate trigonometric series to approximate the value of each function to four decimal places. Then, compare the approximation to the actual value.*

**7.** $\sin \frac{\pi}{2}$

**8.** $\cos \frac{\pi}{4}$

**9.** $\cos \frac{\pi}{3}$

*Write each expression or complex number in exponential form.*

**10.** $5 + 5i$

**11.** $1 - \sqrt{3}i$

**12.** $13\left(\cos \frac{\pi}{3} + i \sin \frac{\pi}{3}\right)$

**13.** $7\left(\cos \frac{7\pi}{6} + i \sin \frac{7\pi}{6}\right)$

*Find each value.*

**14.** $\ln(-5)$

**15.** $\ln(-5.7)$

**16.** $\ln(-1000)$

Glencoe Division, Macmillan/McGraw-Hill

# 12-7 Practice Worksheet

## Special Sequences and Series

Use the first five terms of the exponential series $e^x = 1 + x + \frac{x^2}{2!} + \frac{x^3}{3!} + \frac{x^4}{4!} + \dots$ and a calculator to approximate each value to the nearest hundredth.

**1.** $e^{0.5}$
   **1.65**

**2.** $e^{1.2}$
   **3.29**

**3.** $e^{3.1}$
   **17.72**

**4.** $e^{2.7}$
   **12.84**

**5.** $e^{0.9}$
   **2.45**

**6.** $e^{2.2}$
   **8.37**

Use the first five terms of the appropriate trigonometric series to approximate the value of each function to four decimal places. Then, compare the approximation to the actual value.

**7.** $\sin \frac{\pi}{2}$

   **1.0000; equal**

**8.** $\cos \frac{\pi}{4}$

   **0.7071; equal**

**9.** $\cos \frac{\pi}{3}$

   **0.50000; equal**

Write each expression or complex number in exponential form.

**10.** $5 + 5i$

   $5\sqrt{2}e^{\frac{i\pi}{4}}$

**11.** $1 - \sqrt{3}i$

   $2e^{\frac{4\pi i}{3}}$

**12.** $13\left(\cos \frac{\pi}{3} + i \sin \frac{\pi}{3}\right)$

   $13e^{\frac{i\pi}{3}}$

**13.** $7\left(\cos \frac{7\pi}{6} + i \sin \frac{7\pi}{6}\right)$

   $7e^{\frac{7\pi i}{6}}$

Find each value.

**14.** $\ln(-5)$
   $i\pi + 1.6094$

**15.** $\ln(-5.7)$
   $i\pi + 1.7405$

**16.** $\ln(-1000)$
   $i\pi + 6.9078$

Glencoe Division, Macmillan/McGraw-Hill

12-8 | **Practice Worksheet**

## Mathematical Induction

**Use mathematical induction to prove that each formula is valid for all positive integral values of n.**

1. $\frac{1}{3} + \frac{2}{3} + \frac{3}{3} + \ldots + \frac{n}{3} = \frac{n}{6}(n+1)$

2. $4 + 12 + 36 + \ldots + 4 \cdot 3^{n-1} = 2(3^n - 1)$

Glencoe Division, Macmillan/McGraw-Hill

## 12-8 Practice Worksheet

# Mathematical Induction

**Use mathematical induction to prove that each formula is valid for all positive integral values of n.**

**1.** $\frac{1}{3} + \frac{2}{3} + \frac{3}{3} + \ldots + \frac{n}{3} = \frac{n}{6}(n+1)$

$S_1$: $\frac{1}{3} = \frac{1}{6}(1+1)$, So the formula is valid for $n = 1$.

Assume the formula is valid for $n = k$.

$S_k$: $\frac{1}{3} + \frac{2}{3} + \frac{3}{3} + \cdots + \frac{k}{3} = \frac{k}{6}(k+1)$. Now prove that it is valid

for $n = k + 1$.

$$S_{k+1} = \frac{1}{3} + \frac{2}{3} + \frac{3}{3} + \cdots + \frac{k}{3} + \frac{k+1}{3}$$

$$= \frac{k}{6}(k+1) + \frac{k+1}{3}$$

$$= \frac{k(k+1) + 2(k+1)}{6}$$

$$= \frac{k^2 + 3k + 2}{6} = \frac{(k+1)}{6}(k+2)$$

So, $S_n$ is valid for all positive integers $n$.

**2.** $4 + 12 + 36 + \ldots + 4 \cdot 3^{n-1} = 2(3^n - 1)$

$S_1$: $4 = 2(3^1 - 1)$. So, the formula is valid for $n = 1$.
Assume the formula is valid for $n = k$.
$S_k$: $4 + 12 + 36 + \cdots + 4 \cdot 3^{k-1} = 2(3^k - 1)$. Now prove that
it is valid for $n = k + 1$.

$$S_{k+1} = 4 + 12 + 36 + \cdots + 4 \cdot 3^{k-1} + 4 \cdot 3^k$$

$$= 2(3^k - 1) + 4 \cdot 3^k$$

$$= 2 \cdot 3^k - 2 + 4 \cdot 3^k$$

$$= 3^k(2 + 4) - 2$$

$$= 2 \cdot 3 \cdot 3^k - 2$$

$$= 2(3^{k+1} - 1)$$

Thus, $S_n$ is valid for all positive integers $n$.

Glencoe Division, Macmillan/McGraw-Hill

# 13-1 Practice Worksheet

## *Iterating Functions with Real Numbers*

**Find the first three iterates of each function using the given initial value. If necessary, round your answers to the nearest hundredth.**

**1.** $f(x) = x^2 - 0.5$; $x_0 = 1.5$

**2.** $f(x) = x^2 - 0.5$; $x_0 = -1.5$

**3.** $f(x) = x^3 - 0.5$; $x_0 = 0.75$

**4.** $f(x) = x(2.5 - x)$; $x_0 = 2.1$

**Find the first ten iterates for f(x) = 2.3(1 – x) for each initial value. If necessary, round your answers to the nearest hundredth.**

**5.** $x_0 = 0.3$

**6.** $x_0 = 1.5$

**7.** $x_0 = 0.99$

**8.** $x_0 = -0.5$

**Find the first ten iterates for f(x) = 3.2(1 – x) for each initial value. If necessary, round your answers to the nearest hundredth.**

**9.** $x_0 = 0.25$

**10.** $x_0 = 0.09$

**11.** $x_0 = 0.75$

**12.** $x_0 = 0$

Glencoe Division, Macmillan/McGraw-Hill

## 13-1 | Practice Worksheet

## Iterating Functions with Real Numbers

Find the first three iterates of each function using the given initial value. If necessary, round your answers to the nearest hundredth.

**1.** $f(x) = x^2 - 0.5$; $x_0 = 1.5$
**1.75, 2.56, 6.05**

**2.** $f(x) = x^2 - 0.5$; $x_0 = -1.5$
**1.75, 2.56, 6.05**

**3.** $f(x) = x^3 - 0.5$; $x_0 = 0.75$
**−0.08, −0.50, −0.63**

**4.** $f(x) = x(2.5 - x)$; $x_0 = 2.1$
**0.84, 1.39, 1.54**

Find the first ten iterates for $f(x) = 2.3(1 - x)$ for each initial value. If necessary, round your answers to the nearest hundredth.

**5.** $x_0 = 0.3$
**1.61, −1.40, 5.52, −10.40, 26.22, −58.01, 135.72, −309.86, 714.98, −1642.15**

**6.** $x_0 = 1.5$
**−1.15, 4.95, −9.09, 23.21, −51.08, 119.78, −273.19, 630.64, −1448.17, 3333.09**

**7.** $x_0 = 0.99$
**0.02, 2.25, −2.88, 8.92, −18.22, 44.21, −99.38, 230.87, −528.70, 1218.31**

**8.** $x_0 = -0.5$
**3.45, −5.64, 15.27, −32.82, 77.79, −176.62, 408.53, −937.32, 2158.14, −4961.42**

Find the first ten iterates for $f(x) = 3.2(1 - x)$ for each initial value. If necessary, round your answers to the nearest hundredth.

**9.** $x_0 = 0.25$
**2.4, −4.48, 17.54, −52.93, 172.58, −549.06, 1760.19, −5629.41, 18,017.31, −57,652.19**

**10.** $x_0 = 0.09$
**2.92, −6.11, 22.75, −69.60, 225.92, −719.74, 2306.37, −7377.18, 23,610.18, −75,549.38**

**11.** $x_0 = 0.75$
**0.8, 0.64, 1.15, −0.48, 4.74, −11.97, 41.50, −129.60, 417.92, −1334.14**

**12.** $x_0 = 0$
**3.2, −7.04, 25.73, −79.14, 256.45, −817.44, 2619.01, −8377.63, 26,811.62, −85, 793.98**

Glencoe Division, Macmillan/McGraw-Hill

**13-2** | # Practice Worksheet

## Graphical Iteration of Linear Functions

*Copy the graphs shown and perform graphical iteration for the first four iterates of the initial point shown.*

**1.**

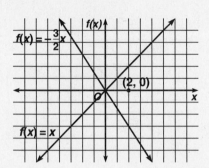

**2.**

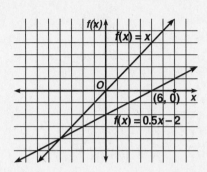

*Graph each function and the function f(x) = x on the same set of axes. Then perform graphical iteration for $x_0 = 1$. State the slope of the linear function and the type of path that the graphical iteration forms.*

**3.** $f(x) = 2x + 1$

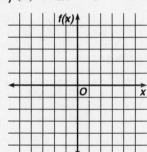

**4.** $f(x) = -0.5x + 1$

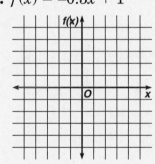

**5.** $f(x) = 0.4x - 2$

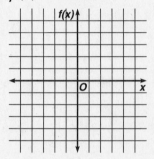

*Find the coordinates of the fixed point for each function. Is the x-coordinate of the fixed point a repeller or an attractor?*

**6.** $f(x) = 3.5x - 4$

**7.** $f(x) = -2x + 3$

**8.** $f(x) = 0.6x - 5$

**9.** $f(x) = -0.45x + 3$

Glencoe Division, Macmillan/McGraw-Hill

**13-2**  **Practice Worksheet**

## Graphical Iteration of Linear Functions

*Copy the graphs shown and perform graphical iteration for the first four iterates of the initial point shown.*

**1.**

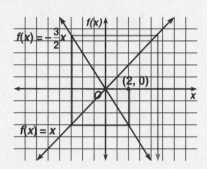

**2.**

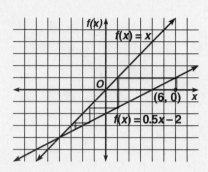

*Graph each function and the function f(x) = x on the same set of axes. Then perform graphical iteration for $x_0 = 1$. State the slope of the linear function and the type of path that the graphical iteration forms.*

**3.** $f(x) = 2x + 1$

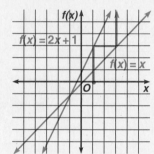

**2, staircase out**

**4.** $f(x) = -0.5x + 1$

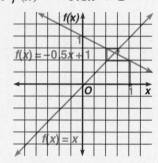

**−0.5, spiral in**

**5.** $f(x) = 0.4x - 2$

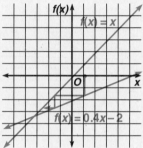

**0.4 staircase in**

*Find the coordinates of the fixed point for each function. Is the x-coordinate of the fixed point a repeller or an attractor?*

**6.** $f(x) = 3.5x - 4$
**(1.6, 1.6), repeller**

**7.** $f(x) = -2x + 3$
**(1,1), repeller**

**8.** $f(x) = 0.6x - 5$
**(−12.5, −12.5), attractor**

**9.** $f(x) = -0.45x + 3$
$\left( \dfrac{60}{29}, \dfrac{60}{29} \right)$, **attractor**

**13-3** **Practice Worksheet**

## Graphical Iteration of the Logistic Function

*Find the coordinates of the vertex of the graph of each logistic function.*

**1.** $f(x) = 3.6x(1 - x)$

**2.** $f(x) = 0.25x(1 - x)$

**3.** $f(x) = 2.3x(1 - x)$

**4.** $f(x) = 0.76x(1 - x)$

*Find the coordinates of the fixed points for each function. Use the graphical iteration behavior program on pages 724-725 of your textbook to graph the function and determine if the x-coordinate of each nonzero fixed point is a repeller or an attractor.*

**5.** $f(x) = 2.5x(1 - x)$

**6.** $f(x) = 0.6x(1 - x)$

**7.** $f(x) = 0.5x(1 - x)$

**8.** $f(x) = 2.0x(1 - x)$

*Use the modified graphical iteration behavior program on pages 724-725 of your textbook to determine the long-term iterative behavior of the function $f(x) = ax(1 - x)$ for each value of a. Write period-n attractor, fixed point attractor, or chaos.*

**9.** $a = 3.21$

**10.** $a = 2.1$

**11.** $a = 4.0$

**12.** $a = 2.25$

**13.** $a = 3.47$

**14.** $a = 1.9$

# 13-3 Practice Worksheet

## Graphical Iteration of the Logistic Function

**Find the coordinates of the vertex of the graph of each logistic function.**

**1.** $f(x) = 3.6x(1 - x)$

$$\left(\frac{1}{2}, 0.9\right)$$

**2.** $f(x) = 0.25x(1 - x)$

$$\left(\frac{1}{2}, 0.0625\right)$$

**3.** $f(x) = 2.3x(1 - x)$

$$\left(\frac{1}{2}, 0.575\right)$$

**4.** $f(x) = 0.76x(1 - x)$

$$\left(\frac{1}{2}, 0.19\right)$$

**Find the coordinates of the fixed points for each function. Use the graphical iteration behavior program on pages 724-725 of your textbook to graph the function and determine if the x-coordinate of each nonzero fixed point is a repeller or an attractor.**

**5.** $f(x) = 2.5x(1 - x)$

$(0, 0)$; $\left(\frac{3}{5}, \frac{3}{5}\right)$; attractor

**6.** $f(x) = 0.6x(1 - x)$

$(0, 0)$; $\left(-\frac{2}{3}, -\frac{2}{3}\right)$; repeller

**7.** $f(x) = 0.5x(1 - x)$

$(0,0)$; $(-1, -1)$; repeller

**8.** $f(x) = 2.0x(1 - x)$

$(0, 0)$; $\left(\frac{1}{2}, \frac{1}{2}\right)$; attractor

**Use the modified graphical iteration behavior program on pages 724-725 of your textbook to determine the long-term iterative behavior of the function $f(x) = ax(1 - x)$ for each value of a. Write period-n attractor, fixed point attractor, or chaos.**

**9.** $a = 3.21$

period –2
attractor

**10.** $a = 2.1$

fixed point
attractor

**11.** $a = 4.0$

chaos

**12.** $a = 2.25$

fixed point
attractor

**13.** $a = 3.47$

period 4
attractor

**14.** $a = 1.9$

fixed point
attractor

Glencoe Division, Macmillan/McGraw-Hill

**13-4** **Practice Worksheet**

## Complex Numbers and Iteration

**Find the first three iterates of the function $f(z) = 3z - i$ for each initial value.**

**1.** $z_0 = 1 + 2i$              **2.** $z_0 = -5i$              **3.** $z_0 = 4$

**4.** $z_0 = 3 - i$              **5.** $z_0 = 0.5 - 0.25i$          **6.** $z_0 = 0.2i$

**Find the first three iterates of the function $f(z) = 2z - (3 + i)$ for each initial value.**

**7.** $z_0 = 1 - 2i$             **8.** $z_0 = -2 - 5i$            **9.** $z_0 = 3 - i$

**10.** $z_0 = 0.5 + i$           **11.** $z_0 = i$               **12.** $z_0 = 1 - i$

**Find the next four iterates of the function $f(z) = z^2 + c$ for each given value of c and each initial value.**

**13.** $c = 1 - 2i; z_0 = 0$        **14.** $c = i; z_0 = i$          **15.** $c = 2 - 3i; z_0 = 1 + i$

## 13-4 Practice Worksheet

### Complex Numbers and Iteration

Find the first three iterates of the function $f(z) = 3z - i$ for each initial value.

1. $z_0 = 1 + 2i$
   $3 + 5i$
   $9 + 14i$
   $27 + 41i$

2. $z_0 = -5i$
   $-16i$
   $-49i$
   $-148i$

3. $z_0 = 4$
   $12 - i$
   $36 - 4i$
   $108 - 13i$

4. $z_0 = 3 - i$
   $9 - 4i$
   $27 - 13i$
   $81 - 40i$

5. $z_0 = 0.5 - 0.25i$
   $1.5 - 1.75i$
   $4.5 - 6.25i$
   $13.5 - 19.75i$

6. $z_0 = 0.2i$
   $-0.4i$
   $-2.2i$
   $-7.6i$

Find the first three iterates of the function $f(z) = 2z - (3 + i)$ for each initial value.

7. $z_0 = 1 - 2i$
   $-1 - 5i$
   $-5 - 11i$
   $-13 - 23i$

8. $z_0 = -2 - 5i$
   $-7 - 11i$
   $-17 - 23i$
   $-37 - 47i$

9. $z_0 = 3 - i$
   $3 - 3i$
   $3 - 7i$
   $3 - 15i$

10. $z_0 = 0.5 + i$
    $-2 + i$
    $-7 + i$
    $-17 + i$

11. $z_0 = i$
    $-3 + i$
    $-9 + i$
    $-21 + i$

12. $z_0 = 1 - i$
    $-1 - 3i$
    $-5 - 7i$
    $-13 - 15i$

Find the next four iterates of the function $f(z) = z^2 + c$ for each given value of c and each initial value.

13. $c = 1 - 2i; z_0 = 0$
    $1 - 2i$
    $-2 - 6i$
    $-31 + 22i$
    $478 - 1366i$

14. $c = i; z_0 = i$
    $-1 + i$
    $-i$
    $-1 + i$
    $-i$

15. $c = 2 - 3i; z_0 = 1 + i$
    $2 - i$
    $5 - 7i$
    $-22 - 73i$
    $-4843 + 3209i$

## 13-5 Practice Worksheet

# Escape Points, Prisoner Points, and Julia Sets

**Determine whether the graph of each value is in the prisoner set or the escape set for the function** $f(z) = z^2 + (-3 + 0i)$.

**1.** $0.5 + 0.5i$

**2.** $0$

**3.** $\dfrac{1 + \sqrt{13}}{2}$

**Determine whether the graph of each value is in the prisoner set or the escape set for the function** $f(z) = z^2 + (-2 + 0i)$.

**4.** $1 + 2i$

**5.** $3 - 2i$

**6.** $2.0 + 0i$

**Determine whether the Julia set for each function is connected or disconnected.**

**7.** $f(z) = z^2 + (2 + i)$

**8.** $f(z) = z^2 + (-0.2 + 0.05i)$

**9.** $f(z) = z^2 + i$

**10.** $f(z) = z^2 + 1$

**11.** $f(z) = z^2 - 1$

**12.** $f(z) = z^2 + (1 - i)$

## 13-5 Practice Worksheet

## Escape Points, Prisoner Points, and Julia Sets

*Determine whether the graph of each value is in the prisoner set or the escape set*
*for the function f(z) = z² + (−3 + 0i).*

**1.** $0.5 + 0.5i$

escape set

**2.** $0$

escape set

**3.** $\dfrac{1 + \sqrt{13}}{2}$

prisoner set

*Determine whether the graph of each value is in the prisoner set or the escape set*
*for the function f(z) = z² + (−2 + 0i).*

**4.** $1 + 2i$

escape set

**5.** $3 - 2i$

escape set

**6.** $2.0 + 0i$

prisoner set

*Determine whether the Julia set for each function is connected or disconnected.*

**7.** $f(z) = z^2 + (2 + i)$

disconnected

**8.** $f(z) = z^2 + (-0.2 + 0.05i)$

connected

**9.** $f(z) = z^2 + i$

connected

**10.** $f(z) = z^2 + 1$

disconnected

**11.** $f(z) = z^2 - 1$

connected

**12.** $f(z) = z^2 + (1 - i)$

disconnected

Glencoe Division, Macmillan/McGraw-Hill

# Practice Worksheet

## The Mandelbrot Set

For each value of c given, complete the following.

a. Determine whether the Julia set associated with each value of c is connected or disconnected.

b. Determine if the point is inside or outside of the Mandelbrot set.

c. Use the color scheme given on page 743 in the lesson to assign a color to the point.

**1.** $c = -1$

**2.** $c = -i$

**3.** $c = -0.8 + 0.5i$

**4.** $c = 2 + i$

**5.** $c = -0.4 - 0.6i$

**6.** $c = -0.3 + i$

Glencoe Division, Macmillan/McGraw-Hill

13-6

# Practice Worksheet

## The Mandelbrot Set

*For each value of c given, complete the following.*

a. *Determine whether the Julia set associated with each value of c is connected or disconnected.*

b. *Determine if the point is inside or outside of the Mandelbrot set.*

c. *Use the color scheme given on page 743 in the lesson to assign a color to the point.*

**1.** $c = -1$
   connected,
   inside,
   black

**2.** $c = -i$
   connected,
   inside,
   black

**3.** $c = -0.8 + 0.5i$
   disconnected,
   outside,
   light blue

**4.** $c = 2 + i$
   disconnected,
   outside,
   orange

**5.** $c = -0.4 - 0.6i$
   connected,
   inside,
   black

**6.** $c = -0.3 + i$
   disconnected,
   outside,
   light blue

Glencoe Division, Macmillan/McGraw-Hill

# 14-1 Practice Worksheet

## Permutations

### Find each value.

**1.** $P(10, 7)$

**2.** $\dfrac{P(7, 3)}{P(4, 2)}$

**3.** $\dfrac{P(6, 4) \cdot P(5, 2)}{P(7, 4)}$

### Solve.

**4.** A briefcase lock has 3 rotating cylinders, each containing 10 digits. How many numerical codes are possible?

**5.** A golf club manufacturer makes irons with 7 different shaft lengths, 3 different grips, and 2 different club head materials. How many different combinations are offered?

**6.** There are 5 different routes that a commuter can take from her home to the office. In how many ways can she make a round trip if she uses different routes for coming and going?

**7.** In how many ways can the 4 call letters of a radio station be arranged if the first letter must W or K and no letters repeat?

**8.** How many 7-digit telephone numbers can be formed if the first digit cannot be 0 or 1?

**9.** How many 7-digit telephone numbers can be formed if the first digit cannot be 0 or 1 and no digit can be repeated?

# 14-1 **Practice Worksheet**

## *Permutations*

### *Find each value.*

1. $P(10, 7)$

**604,800**

2. $\dfrac{P(7, 3)}{P(4, 2)}$

**17.5**

3. $\dfrac{P(6, 4) \cdot P(5, 2)}{P(7, 4)}$

$\dfrac{60}{7}$

### *Solve.*

4. A briefcase lock has 3 rotating cylinders, each containing 10 digits. How many numerical codes are possible?

**1000**

5. A golf club manufacturer makes irons with 7 different shaft lengths, 3 different grips, and 2 different club head materials. How many different combinations are offered? **42**

6. There are 5 different routes that a commuter can take from her home to the office. In how many ways can she make a round trip if she uses different routes for coming and going? **20**

7. In how many ways can the 4 call letters of a radio station be arranged if the first letter must W or K and no letters repeat? **27,600**

8. How many 7-digit telephone numbers can be formed if the first digit cannot be 0 or 1? **8,000,000**

9. How many 7-digit telephone numbers can be formed if the first digit cannot be 0 or 1 and no digit can be repeated? **483,840**

Glencoe Division, Macmillan/McGraw-Hill

# 14-2 Practice Worksheet

## Permutations with Repetitions and Circular Permutations

*How many different ways can the letters of each word be arranged?*

1. CANADA

2. ILLINI

3. ANNUALLY

4. MEMBERS

*Solve.*

5. A photographer is taking a picture of a bride and groom together with 6 attendants. How many ways can he arrange the 8 people in a line if the bride and groom stand in the middle?

6. A person playing a word game has the following letters in her tray: QUOUNNTAGGRA. How many 12-letter arrangements could she make to check if a single word could be formed from all the letters?

7. How many ways can 3 identical pen sets and 5 identical watches be given to 8 graduates if each person receives one item?

8. Three different hardcover books and five different paperbacks are placed on a shelf. How many ways can they be arranged if all the hardcover books are together?

9. In how many ways can 6 people stand in a ring around the player who is "it"?

10. In how many ways can 5 charms be placed on a bracelet with no clasp?

**14-2** # Practice Worksheet

## Permutations with Repetitions and Circular Permutations

**How many different ways can the letters of each word be arranged?**

1. CANADA
   **120**

2. ILLINI
   **60**

3. ANNUALLY
   **5040**

4. MEMBERS
   **1260**

*Solve.*

5. A photographer is taking a picture of a bride and groom together with 6 attendants. How many ways can he arrange the 8 people in a line if the bride and groom stand in the middle? **1440**

6. A person playing a word game has the following letters in her tray: QUOUNNTAGGRA. How many 12-letter arrangements could she make to check if a single word could be formed from all the letters? **29,937,600**

7. How many ways can 3 identical pen sets and 5 identical watches be given to 8 graduates if each person receives one item? **56**

8. Three different hardcover books and five different paperbacks are placed on a shelf. How many ways can they be arranged if all the hardcover books are together? **4320**

9. In how many ways can 6 people stand in a ring around the player who is "it"? **120**

10. In how many ways can 5 charms be placed on a bracelet with no clasp? **12**

Glencoe Division, Macmillan/McGraw-Hill

# 14-3

# Practice Worksheet

## Combinations

*Evaluate each expression.*

**1.** $C(7, 2)$

**2.** $C(10, 4)$

**3.** $C(8, 8)$

**4.** $C(10, 4) \cdot C(5, 3)$

**5.** $C(12, 4) \cdot C(8, 3)$

**6.** $P(4, 3) \cdot C(8, 6)$

**7.** $P(12, 3) \cdot C(2, 1) \cdot C(6, 5)$

**8.** $P(8, 3) \cdot C(9, 6) \cdot C(8, 2)$

## Solve.

**9.** Sally has 7 candles, each a different color. How many ways can she arrange the candles in a candelabra that holds 3 candles?

**10.** In how many ways can a student choose 4 books from 2 geometry, 4 geography, 5 history, and 2 physics books?

**11.** Eight toppings for pizza are available. In how many ways can Jim choose 3 of the toppings?

**12.** From a list of 12 books, how many groups of 5 books can be selected?

**13.** How many committees of 5 students can be selected from class of 25?

**14.** Leroy can afford to buy 2 of the 6 CDs he wants. How many possible combinations could he buy?

**15.** A box contains 12 black and 8 green marbles. In how many ways can 3 black and 2 green marbles be chosen?

**16.** A box contains 12 black and 8 green marbles. In how many ways can 5 marbles be chosen?

Glencoe Division, Macmillan/McGraw-Hill

14-3 **Practice Worksheet**

## Combinations

*Evaluate each expression.*

**1.** $C(7, 2)$
21

**2.** $C(10, 4)$
210

**3.** $C(8, 8)$
1

**4.** $C(10, 4) \cdot C(5, 3)$
2100

**5.** $C(12, 4) \cdot C(8, 3)$
27,720

**6.** $P(4, 3) \cdot C(8, 6)$
672

**7.** $P(12, 3) \cdot C(2, 1) \cdot C(6, 5)$
15,840

**8.** $P(8, 3) \cdot C(9, 6) \cdot C(8, 2)$
790,272

*Solve.*

**9.** Sally has 7 candles, each a different color. How many ways can she arrange the candles in a candelabra that holds 3 candles? **210**

**10.** In how many ways can a student choose 4 books from 2 geometry, 4 geography, 5 history, and 2 physics books? **715**

**11.** Eight toppings for pizza are available. In how many ways can Jim choose 3 of the toppings? **56**

**12.** From a list of 12 books, how many groups of 5 books can be selected? **792**

**13.** How many committees of 5 students can be selected from class of 25? **53,130**

**14.** Leroy can afford to buy 2 of the 6 CDs he wants. How many possible combinations could he buy? **15**

**15.** A box contains 12 black and 8 green marbles. In how many ways can 3 black and 2 green marbles be chosen? **6160**

**16.** A box contains 12 black and 8 green marbles. In how many ways can 5 marbles be chosen? **15,504**

Glencoe Division, Macmillan/McGraw-Hill

## 14-4 Practice Worksheet

### Probability and Odds

*A bag contains 7 pennies, 4 nickels, and 5 dimes. Three coins are selected at random. Find the probability of each selection.*

**1.** all 3 pennies

**2.** all 3 nickels

**3.** all 3 dimes

**4.** 2 pennies, 1 dime

**5.** 1 penny, 1 dime, 1 nickel

**6.** 1 dime, 2 nickels

*A bag contains 5 red, 9 blue, and 6 white marbles. Two are selected at random. Find the probability of each selection.*

**7.** 2 red

**8.** 2 blue

**9.** 1 red, 1 blue

**10.** 1 red, 1 white

*Sharon has 8 mystery books and 9 science-fiction books. Four are selected at random. Find the probability of each selection.*

**11.** 4 mystery books

**12.** 4 science-fiction books

**13.** 2 mysteries, 2 science-fiction

**14.** 3 mysteries, 1 science-fiction

*From a standard deck of cards, 5 cards are drawn. What are the odds of each selection?*

**15.** 5 aces

**16.** 5 face cards

**17.** 5 from one suit

**18.** 2 of one suit, 3 of another

NAME _____ DATE _____

# Practice Worksheet

## Probability and Odds

**A bag contains 7 pennies, 4 nickels, and 5 dimes. Three coins are selected at random. Find the probability of each selection.**

**1.** all 3 pennies
$$\frac{1}{16}$$

**2.** all 3 nickels
$$\frac{1}{140}$$

**3.** all 3 dimes
$$\frac{1}{56}$$

**4.** 2 pennies, 1 dime
$$\frac{3}{16}$$

**5.** 1 penny, 1 dime, 1 nickel
$$\frac{1}{4}$$

**6.** 1 dime, 2 nickels
$$\frac{3}{56}$$

**A bag contains 5 red, 9 blue, and 6 white marbles. Two are selected at random. Find the probability of each selection.**

**7.** 2 red
$$\frac{1}{19}$$

**8.** 2 blue
$$\frac{18}{95}$$

**9.** 1 red, 1 blue
$$\frac{9}{38}$$

**10.** 1 red, 1 white
$$\frac{3}{19}$$

**Sharon has 8 mystery books and 9 science-fiction books. Four are selected at random. Find the probability of each selection.**

**11.** 4 mystery books
$$\frac{1}{34}$$

**12.** 4 science-fiction books
$$\frac{9}{170}$$

**13.** 2 mysteries, 2 science-fiction
$$\frac{36}{85}$$

**14.** 3 mysteries, 1 science-fiction
$$\frac{18}{85}$$

**From a standard deck of cards, 5 cards are drawn. What are the odds of each selection?**

**15.** 5 aces
$$0$$

**16.** 5 face cards
$$\frac{33}{108,257}$$

**17.** 5 from one suit
$$\frac{33}{16,627}$$

**18.** 2 of one suit, 3 of another
$$\frac{429}{7901}$$

Glencoe Division, Macmillan/McGraw-Hill

# 14-5 Practice Worksheet

## Probability of Independent and Dependent Events

*There are 3 nickels, 2 dimes, and 5 quarters in a purse. Three coins are selected in succession at random.*

**1.** Find the probability of selecting 1 nickel, 1 dime, and 1 quarter in that order without replacement.

**2.** Find the probability of selecting 1 nickel, 1 dime, and 1 quarter in that order with replacement.

**3.** Find the probability of selecting 1 nickel, 1 dime, and 1 quarter in any order with replacement.

**4.** Find the probability of selecting 1 nickel, 1 dime, and 1 quarter in any order without replacement.

*A red, a green, and a yellow die are tossed. What is the probability that the following occurs?*

**5.** All 3 dice show a 4.

**6.** None of the 3 dice shows a 4.

**7.** The red die shows an even number, and the other 2 show different odd numbers.

**8.** All 3 dice show the same number.

*From a standard deck of 52 cards, 2 cards are selected. What is the probability that the following occurs?*

**9.** 2 black cards selected without replacement

**10.** 2 black cards selected with replacement

**11.** 1 red card and 1 spade in any order selected without replacement

**12.** 1 red card and 1 spade in that order selected without replacement

Glencoe Division, Macmillan/McGraw-Hill

# 14-5 Practice Worksheet

## Probability of Independent and Dependent Events

**There are 3 nickels, 2 dimes, and 5 quarters in a purse. Three coins are selected in succession at random.**

1. Find the probability of selecting 1 nickel, 1 dime, and 1 quarter in that order without replacement.

   $\dfrac{1}{24}$

2. Find the probability of selecting 1 nickel, 1 dime, and 1 quarter in that order with replacement.

   $\dfrac{3}{100}$

3. Find the probability of selecting 1 nickel, 1 dime, and 1 quarter in any order with replacement.

   $\dfrac{9}{50}$

4. Find the probability of selecting 1 nickel, 1 dime, and 1 quarter in any order without replacement.

   $\dfrac{1}{4}$

**A red, a green, and a yellow die are tossed. What is the probability that the following occurs?**

5. All 3 dice show a 4.

   $\dfrac{1}{216}$

6. None of the 3 dice shows a 4.

   $\dfrac{125}{216}$

7. The red die shows an even number, and the other 2 show different odd numbers.

   $\dfrac{1}{12}$

8. All 3 dice show the same number.

   $\dfrac{1}{36}$

**From a standard deck of 52 cards, 2 cards are selected. What is the probability that the following occurs?**

9. 2 black cards selected without replacement

   $\dfrac{25}{102}$

10. 2 black cards selected with replacement

    $\dfrac{1}{4}$

11. 1 red card and 1 spade in any order selected without replacement

    $\dfrac{13}{51}$

12. 1 red card and 1 spade in that order selected without replacement

    $\dfrac{13}{102}$

Glencoe Division, Macmillan/McGraw-Hill

## 14-6 Practice Worksheet

### Probability of Mutually Exclusive or Inclusive Events

*An urn contains 7 white marbles and 5 blue marbles. Four marbles are selected without replacement. What is the probability that each occurs?*

1. all white or all blue

2. exactly 3 white

3. at least 3 white

4. exactly 3 white or exactly 3 blue

*Two cards are drawn from a standard deck of 52 cards. What is the probability that each occurs?*

5. 2 spades

6. 2 spades or 2 red cards

7. 2 red cards or 2 jacks

8. 2 spades or 2 face cards

*Three dice are tossed. What is the probability that each occurs?*

9. exactly two 5s

10. at least two 5s

11. three 5s

12. no 5s

**14-6** # Practice Worksheet

## Probability of Mutually Exclusive or Inclusive Events

*An urn contains 7 white marbles and 5 blue marbles. Four marbles are selected without replacement. What is the probability that each occurs?*

**1.** all white or all blue

$\dfrac{8}{99}$

**2.** exactly 3 white

$\dfrac{35}{99}$

**3.** at least 3 white

$\dfrac{14}{33}$

**4.** exactly 3 white or exactly 3 blue

$\dfrac{49}{99}$

*Two cards are drawn from a standard deck of 52 cards. What is the probability that each occurs?*

**5.** 2 spades

$\dfrac{1}{17}$

**6.** 2 spades or 2 red cards

$\dfrac{31}{102}$

**7.** 2 red cards or 2 jacks

$\dfrac{55}{221}$

**8.** 2 spades or 2 face cards

$\dfrac{47}{442}$

*Three dice are tossed. What is the probability that each occurs?*

**9.** exactly two 5s

$\dfrac{5}{72}$

**10.** at least two 5s

$\dfrac{2}{27}$

**11.** three 5s

$\dfrac{1}{216}$

**12.** no 5s

$\dfrac{125}{216}$

Glencoe Division, Macmillan/McGraw-Hill

# Practice Worksheet

## Conditional Probability

*A card is drawn from a standard deck of 52 cards and is found to be red. Given that event, find each probability.*

1. $P$ (heart)

2. $P$ (ace)

3. $P$ (face card)

4. $P$ (jack or ten)

5. $P$ (six of spades)

6. $P$ (six of hearts)

*A survey taken at Stirers High School shows that 48% of the respondents liked soccer, 66% liked basketball, and 38% liked hockey. Also, 30% liked soccer and basketball, 22% liked basketball and hockey, and 28% liked soccer and hockey. Finally, 12% liked all three sports. Find each probability.*

7. the probability Meg likes soccer if she likes basketball

8. the probability Juan likes basketball if he likes soccer

9. the probability Kim likes hockey if she likes basketball

10. the probability Greg likes hockey and basketball if he likes soccer

*A pair of dice are thrown. It is known that the sum is greater than seven. Find each probability.*

11. P(numbers match)

12. P(one die shows a 1)

Glencoe Division, Macmillan/McGraw-Hill

# 14-7 Practice Worksheet

## Conditional Probability

*A card is drawn from a standard deck of 52 cards and is found to be red. Given that event, find each probability.*

1. $P$ (heart)

   $\dfrac{1}{2}$

2. $P$ (ace)

   $\dfrac{1}{13}$

3. $P$ (face card)

   $\dfrac{3}{13}$

4. $P$ (jack or ten)

   $\dfrac{2}{13}$

5. $P$ (six of spades)

   $0$

6. $P$ (six of hearts)

   $\dfrac{1}{26}$

*A survey taken at Stirers High School shows that 48% of the respondents liked soccer, 66% liked basketball, and 38% liked hockey. Also, 30% liked soccer and basketball, 22% liked basketball and hockey, and 28% liked soccer and hockey. Finally, 12% liked all three sports. Find each probability.*

7. the probability Meg likes soccer if she likes basketball

   $\dfrac{5}{11}$

8. the probability Juan likes basketball if he likes soccer

   $\dfrac{5}{8}$

9. the probability Kim likes hockey if she likes basketball

   $\dfrac{1}{3}$

10. the probability Greg likes hockey and basketball if he likes soccer

    $\dfrac{1}{4}$

*A pair of dice are thrown. It is known that the sum is greater than seven. Find each probability.*

11. P(numbers match)

    $\dfrac{1}{5}$

12. P(one die shows a 1)

    $0$

Glencoe Division, Macmillan/McGraw-Hill

# 14-8 | Practice Worksheet

## The Binomial Theorem and Probability

*Six coins are tossed. What is the probability that each occurs?*

**1.** 3 heads and 3 tails

**2.** at least 4 heads

**3.** 2 heads or 3 tails

**4.** all heads or all tails

*The probability of Chris making a free throw is $\frac{2}{3}$. If she shoots five times, what is the probability of each?*

**5.** all missed

**6.** all made

**7.** exactly 4 made

**8.** at least 3 made

*When Mary and Dwayne play a certain board game, the probability that Mary will win a game is $\frac{3}{4}$. If they play five games, find the probability of each event.*

**9.** Dwayne wins only once

**10.** Mary wins exactly twice

**11.** Dwayne wins at least two games

**12.** Mary wins at least three games

## 14-8 Practice Worksheet

### *The Binomial Theorem and Probability*

**Six coins are tossed. What is the probability that each occurs?**

**1.** 3 heads and 3 tails

$\dfrac{5}{16}$

**2.** at least 4 heads

$\dfrac{11}{32}$

**3.** 2 heads or 3 tails

$\dfrac{35}{64}$

**4.** all heads or all tails

$\dfrac{1}{32}$

**The probability of Chris making a free throw is $\frac{2}{3}$. If she shoots five times, what is the probability of each?**

**5.** all missed

$\dfrac{1}{243}$

**6.** all made

$\dfrac{32}{243}$

**7.** exactly 4 made

$\dfrac{80}{243}$

**8.** at least 3 made

$\dfrac{64}{81}$

**When Mary and Dwayne play a certain board game, the probability that Mary will win a game is $\frac{3}{4}$. If they play five games, find the probability of each event.**

**9.** Dwayne wins only once

$\dfrac{405}{1024}$

**10.** Mary wins exactly twice

$\dfrac{45}{512}$

**11.** Dwayne wins at least two games

$\dfrac{47}{128}$

**12.** Mary wins at least three games

$\dfrac{459}{512}$

Glencoe Division, Macmillan/McGraw-Hill

NAME _____ DATE _____

# Practice Worksheet

## The Frequency Distribution

The selling prices of a random sample of 30 single-family homes sold in a city during the past year are given below.

| | | | | | |
|---|---|---|---|---|---|
| 67,500 | 72,000 | 54,600 | 38,900 | 87,400 | 28,300 |
| 105,000 | 91,600 | 46,500 | 62,800 | 136,600 | 81,200 |
| 59,900 | 76,200 | 117,100 | 64,400 | 25,500 | 51,800 |
| 88,000 | 63,900 | 125,000 | 70,500 | 28,200 | 59,500 |
| 118,700 | 81,100 | 42,600 | 57,300 | 77,700 | 64,800 |

1. Make a frequency distribution of the data using six classes from $20,000 to $140,000.

2. List the class marks.

3. What are the class intervals?

4. What are the class limits?

5. Which class interval had the greatest frequency?

The ages of 100 people attending a concert are given below.

| Class Limits | 10 - 13 | 13 - 16 | 16 - 19 | 19 - 22 | 22 - 25 |
|---|---|---|---|---|---|
| Frequency | 4 | 19 | 28 | 36 | 13 |

6. List the class marks.
7. What is the class interval?
8. What are the class limits?
9. Which age group had the most people in attendance?
10. Which age group had the fewest people in attendance?

Glencoe Division, Macmillan/McGraw-Hill

# 15-1

# Practice Worksheet

## The Frequency Distribution

The selling prices of a random sample of 30 single-family homes sold in a city during the past year are given below.

| | | | | | |
|---|---|---|---|---|---|
| 67,500 | 72,000 | 54,600 | 38,900 | 87,400 | 28,300 |
| 105,000 | 91,600 | 46,500 | 62,800 | 136,600 | 81,200 |
| 59,900 | 76,200 | 117,100 | 64,400 | 25,500 | 51,800 |
| 88,000 | 63,900 | 125,000 | 70,500 | 28,200 | 59,500 |
| 118,700 | 81,100 | 42,600 | 57,300 | 77,700 | 64,800 |

1. Make a frequency distribution of the data using six classes from $20,000 to $140,000.

| CLASS LIMITS | TALLY | FREQUENCY |
|---|---|---|
| $20,000 - 40,000 | IIII | 4 |
| $40,000 - 60,000 | HHT II | 7 |
| $60,000 - 80,000 | HHT IIII | 9 |
| $80,000 - 100,000 | HHT | 5 |
| $100,000 - 120,000 | III | 3 |
| $120,000 - 140,000 | II | 2 |

2. List the class marks. **$30,000, $50,000, $70,000, $90,000, $110,000, $130,000**

3. What are the class intervals? **$20,000-40,000, $40,000-60,000, $60,000-80,000, $80,000-100,000, $100,000-120,000, $120,000-140,000**

4. What are the class limits? **$20,000, $40,000, $60,000, $80,000, $100,000, $120,000, $140,000**

5. Which class interval had the greatest frequency? **$60,000-80,000**

The ages of 100 people attending a concert are given below.

| Class Limits | 10 - 13 | 13 - 16 | 16 - 19 | 19 - 22 | 22 - 25 |
|---|---|---|---|---|---|
| Frequency | 4 | 19 | 28 | 36 | 13 |

6. List the class marks. **11.5, 14.5, 17.5, 20.5, 23.5**
7. What is the class interval? **3**
8. What are the class limits? **10, 13, 16, 19, 22, 25**
9. Which age group had the most people in attendance? **19-22**
10. Which age group had the fewest people in attendance? **10-13**

Glencoe Division, Macmillan/McGraw-Hill

# 15-2 Practice Worksheet

## Measures of Central Tendency

**The numbers of airline fatalities in the United States during the years 1981 to 1990 are given below.**

| Year | Fatalities | Year | Fatalities |
|------|-----------|------|-----------|
| 1981 | 4 | 1986 | 1 |
| 1982 | 233 | 1987 | 231 |
| 1983 | 15 | 1988 | 285 |
| 1984 | 4 | 1989 | 278 |
| 1985 | 197 | 1990 | 39 |

1. Find the mean of the data.
2. Find the median of the data.
3. Find the mode of the data.

**The average number of points per game scored by members of a basketball team during a recent year are given below.**

| | | |
|------|------|------|
| 37.1 | 8.5 | 4.2 |
| 14.5 | 8.5 | 3.5 |
| 11.3 | 8.3 | 2.8 |
| 9.7 | 6.9 | 1.9 |

4. Find the mean of the data.
5. Find the median of the data.
6. Find the mode of the data.

**The numbers of students present at each monthly meeting of the Spirit Club are given below.**

| | | | |
|-----------|-----|----------|-----|
| August | 146 | January | 121 |
| September | 138 | February | 93 |
| October | 120 | March | 118 |
| November | 132 | April | 129 |
| December | 146 | May | 136 |

7. Find the mean of the data.
8. Find the median of the data.
9. Find the mode of the data.

Glencoe Division, Macmillan/McGraw-Hill

# Practice Worksheet

## Measures of Central Tendency

**The numbers of airline fatalities in the United States during the years 1981 to 1990 are given below.**

| Year | Fatalities | Year | Fatalities |
|------|-----------|------|-----------|
| 1981 | 4 | 1986 | 1 |
| 1982 | 233 | 1987 | 231 |
| 1983 | 15 | 1988 | 285 |
| 1984 | 4 | 1989 | 278 |
| 1985 | 197 | 1990 | 39 |

1. Find the mean of the data. **128.7**
2. Find the median of the data. **118**
3. Find the mode of the data. **4**

**The average number of points per game scored by members of a basketball team during a recent year are given below.**

| | | |
|------|------|------|
| 37.1 | 8.5 | 4.2 |
| 14.5 | 8.5 | 3.5 |
| 11.3 | 8.3 | 2.8 |
| 9.7 | 6.9 | 1.9 |

4. Find the mean of the data. **9.8**
5. Find the median of the data. **8.4**
6. Find the mode of the data. **8.5**

**The numbers of students present at each monthly meeting of the Spirit Club are given below.**

| Month | | Month | |
|-----------|-----|----------|-----|
| August | 146 | January | 121 |
| September | 138 | February | 93 |
| October | 120 | March | 118 |
| November | 132 | April | 129 |
| December | 146 | May | 136 |

7. Find the mean of the data. **127.9**
8. Find the median of the data. **130.5**
9. Find the mode of the data. **146**

Glencoe Division, Macmillan/McGraw-Hill

# 15-3 Practice Worksheet

## *Measures of Variability*

**Find the mean deviation, semi-interquartile range, and standard deviation for each set of data. Make a box-and-whisker plot for each set of data.**

1. 43, 26, 92, 11, 8, 49, 52, 126, 86, 42, 63, 78, 91, 79, 86

2. 1.6, 9.8, 4.5, 6.2, 8.7, 5.6, 3.9, 6.8, 9.7, 1.1, 4.7, 3.8, 7.5, 2.8, 0.1

3. 146, 289, 121, 146, 212, 98, 86, 153, 128, 136, 181, 142

4. 1592, 1486, 1479, 1682, 1720, 1104, 1486, 1895, 1890, 2687, 2450

5. 506, 612, 789, 412, 814, 583, 102, 881, 457, 826

6. 26.8, 15.7, 98.4, 27.3, 14.1, 81.6, 19.4, 21.5, 46.5, 23.7, 16.7, 29.8

Glencoe Division, Macmillan/McGraw-Hill

**15-3** Practice Worksheet

## Measures of Variability

*Find the mean deviation, semi-interquartile range, and standard deviation for each set of data. Make a box-and-whisker plot for each set of data.*

**1.** 43, 26, 92, 11, 8, 49, 52, 126, 86, 42, 63, 78, 91, 79, 86

**27.2; 22; 32.02**

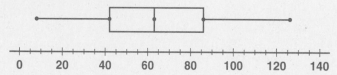

**2.** 1.6, 9.8, 4.5, 6.2, 8.7, 5.6, 3.9, 6.8, 9.7, 1.1, 4.7, 3.8, 7.5, 2.8, 0.1

**2.46; 2.35; 2.93**

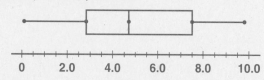

**3.** 146, 289, 121, 146, 212, 98, 86, 153, 128, 136, 181, 142

**37.1; 21.25; 51.99**

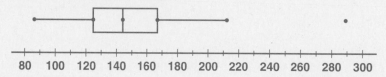

**4.** 1592, 1486, 1479, 1682, 1720, 1104, 1486, 1895, 1890, 2687, 2450

**334.84; 204.5; 433.25**

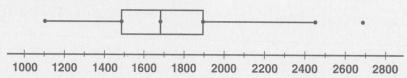

**5.** 506, 612, 789, 412, 814, 583, 102, 881, 457, 826

**186.2; 178.5; 229.04**

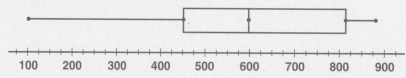

**6.** 26.8, 15.7, 98.4, 27.3, 14.1, 81.6, 19.4, 21.5, 46.5, 23.7, 16.7, 29.8

**20.19; 10.05; 26.10**

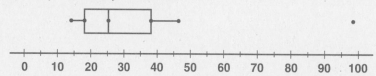

Glencoe Division, Macmillan/McGraw-Hill

**15-4** **Practice Worksheet**

## The Normal Distribution

*A set of 1000 values has a normal distribution. The mean of the data is 120, and the standard deviation is 20.*

1. How many values are within one standard deviation from the mean?

2. What percent of the data is in the range 110 to 130?

3. What percent of the data is in the range 90 to 110?

4. Find the range about the mean which includes 90% of the data.

5. Find the range about the mean which includes 77% of the data.

6. Find the probability that a value selected at random from the data will be within the limits 100 and 150.

7. Find the probability that a value selected at random from the data will be greater than 140.

8. Find the point below which 90% of the data lie.

15-4 **Practice Worksheet**

## The Normal Distribution

*A set of 1000 values has a normal distribution. The mean of the data is 120, and the standard deviation is 20.*

1. How many values are within one standard deviation from the mean?  **683**

2. What percent of the data is in the range 110 to 130?  **38.3%**

3. What percent of the data is in the range 90 to 110?  **24.15%**

4. Find the range about the mean which includes 90% of the data.  **87 to 153**

5. Find the range about the mean which includes 77% of the data.  **96 to 144**

6. Find the probability that a value selected at random from the data will be within the limits 100 and 150.  **0.7745**

7. Find the probability that a value selected at random from the data will be greater than 140.  **0.1585**

8. Find the point below which 90% of the data lie.  **146**

Glencoe Division, Macmillan/McGraw-Hill

## 15-5 Practice Worksheet

### Sample Sets of Data

**Find the standard error of the mean for each sample. Then find the range for a 1% level of confidence and the range for a 5% level of confidence.**

1. $\sigma = 50, N = 100, \overline{X} = 250$

2. $\sigma = 4, N = 64, \overline{X} = 100$

3. $\sigma = 2.6, N = 100, \overline{X} = 50$

4. $\sigma = 43, N = 100, \overline{X} = 110$

**The table below shows a frequency distribution of the time in minutes required for students to wash a car during the car wash. The distribution is a random sample of 250 cars.**

| Number of Minutes | 5 | 6 | 7 | 8 | 9 | 10 |
|---|---|---|---|---|---|---|
| Number of Cars | 2 | 4 | 5 | 1 | 8 | 5 |

5. Find the standard deviation of the data in the frequency distribution.

6. Find the standard error of the mean.

7. Find the interval about the sample mean such that the probability is 0.90 that the true mean lies within the interval.

8. Find the interval about the sample mean such that the probability is 0.95 that the true mean lies within the interval.

## 15-5 | Practice Worksheet

### Sample Sets of Data

**Find the standard error of the mean for each sample. Then find the range for a 1% level of confidence and the range for a 5% level of confidence.**

**1.** $\sigma = 50, N = 100, \overline{X} = 250$
   **5; 237.1−262.9; 240.2−259.8**

**2.** $\sigma = 4, N = 64, \overline{X} = 100$
   **0.5; 98.71−101.29;**
   **99.02−100.98**

**3.** $\sigma = 2.6, N = 100, \overline{X} = 50$

   **0.26; 49.3292−50.6708;**
   **49.4904−50.5096**

**4.** $\sigma = 43, N = 100, \overline{X} = 110$

   **4.3; 98.906−121.094;**
   **101.572−118.428**

**The table below shows a frequency distribution of the time in minutes required for students to wash a car during the car wash. The distribution is a random sample of 250 cars.**

| Number of Minutes | 5 | 6 | 7 | 8 | 9 | 10 |
|---|---|---|---|---|---|---|
| Number of Cars | 2 | 4 | 5 | 1 | 8 | 5 |

**5.** Find the standard deviation of the data in the frequency distribution. **1.64**

**6.** Find the standard error of the mean. **0.327**

**7.** Find the interval about the sample mean such that the probability is 0.90 that the true mean lies within the interval.
**7.42045-8.49955**

**8.** Find the interval about the sample mean such that the probability is 0.95 that the true mean lies within the interval.
**7.31908-8.60092**

Glencoe Division, Macmillan/McGraw-Hill

# 15-6 | Practice Worksheet

## Scatter Plots

**The table below shows the amount of sales for eight sales representatives and the years of sales experience for each representative.**

| Amount of Sales | $9000 | $6000 | $4000 | $3000 | $3000 | $5000 | $8000 | $2000 |
|---|---|---|---|---|---|---|---|---|
| Years of Experience | 6 | 5 | 3 | 1 | 4 | 3 | 6 | 2 |

**1.** Draw a scatter plot and find a median fit line for the data.

**2.** Use a graphing calculator to plot the data and draw a regression line.

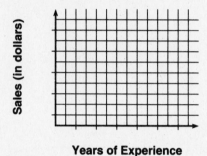

Sales (in dollars)

Years of Experience

**3.** What is the equation of the regression line?

**4.** What is the Pearson product-moment correlation value?

**The table below shows the statistics grades and the economics grades for a group of college students at the end of a given semester.**

| Statistics Grades | 95 | 51 | 49 | 27 | 42 | 52 | 67 | 48 | 46 |
|---|---|---|---|---|---|---|---|---|---|
| Economics Grades | 88 | 70 | 65 | 50 | 60 | 80 | 68 | 49 | 40 |

**5.** Draw a scatter plot and find a median fit line for the data.

**6.** Use a graphing calculator to plot the data and draw a regression line.

Economics Grade

Statistics Grade

**7.** What is the equation of the regression line?

**8.** What is the Pearson product-moment correlation value?

**15-6** | # Practice Worksheet

## Scatter Plots

**The table below shows the amount of sales for eight sales representatives and the years of sales experience for each representative.**

| Amount of Sales | $9000 | $6000 | $4000 | $3000 | $3000 | $5000 | $8000 | $2000 |
|---|---|---|---|---|---|---|---|---|
| Years of Experience | 6 | 5 | 3 | 1 | 4 | 3 | 6 | 2 |

**1.** Draw a scatter plot and find a median fit line for the data.

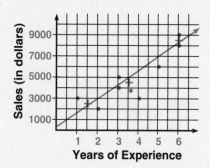

**2.** Use a graphing calculator to plot the data and draw a regression line.

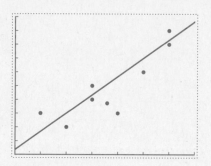

**3.** What is the equation of the regression line?

$y = 1191.5x + 531.9$

**4.** What is the Pearson product-moment correlation value?

0.871

**The table below shows the statistics grades and the economics grades for a group of college students at the end of a given semester.**

| Statistics Grades | 95 | 51 | 49 | 27 | 42 | 52 | 67 | 48 | 46 |
|---|---|---|---|---|---|---|---|---|---|
| Economics Grades | 88 | 70 | 65 | 50 | 60 | 80 | 68 | 49 | 40 |

**5.** Draw a scatter plot and find a median fit line for the data.

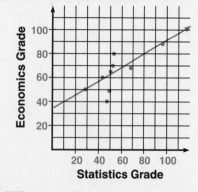

**6.** Use a graphing calculator to plot the data and draw a regression line.

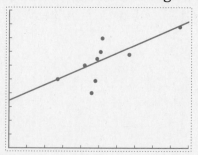

**7.** What is the equation of the regression line?

$y = 0.59x + 32.06$

**8.** What is the Pearson product-moment correlation value?

0.724

Glencoe Division, Macmillan/McGraw-Hill

**16-1**

# Practice Worksheet

## *Graphs*

*Draw each graph described below.*

**1.** $G(4, 7)$

**2.** $G(5, 10)$

**3.** $V = \{A, B, C, D\}, E = \{\{A, B\},$
$\{A, C\}, \{C, D\}\}$

**4.** $V = \{M, N, O, P\}, E = \{\{M, N\},$
$\{M, P\}, \{N, O\}, \{N, P\}, \{O, P\}\}$

**5.** 5 vertices; $\deg(A) = 1, \deg(B) = 2,$
$\deg(C) = 1, \deg(D) = 3, \deg(E) = 4$

**6.** 6 vertices; $\deg(A) = 2, \deg(B) = 1,$
$\deg(C) = 3, \deg(D) = 1, \deg(E) = 1,$
$\deg(F) = 3$

Glencoe Division, Macmillan/McGraw-Hill

16-1 **Practice Worksheet**

## *Graphs*

*Draw each graph described below.*

Sample answers are given.

**1.** $G(4, 7)$

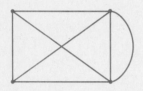

**2.** $G(5, 10)$

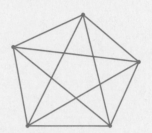

**3.** $V = \{A, B, C, D\}, E = \{\{A, B\},$
   $\{A, C\}, \{C, D\}\}$

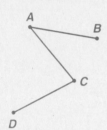

**4.** $V = \{M, N, O, P\}, E = \{\{M, N\},$
   $\{M, P\}, \{N, O\}, \{N, P\}, \{O, P\}\}$

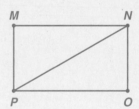

**5.** 5 vertices; $\deg(A) = 1$, $\deg(B) = 2$,
   $\deg(C) = 1$, $\deg(D) = 3$, $\deg(E) = 4$

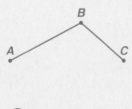

**6.** 6 vertices; $\deg(A) = 2$, $\deg(B) = 1$,
   $\deg(C) = 3$, $\deg(D) = 1$, $\deg(E) = 1$,
   $\deg(F) = 3$

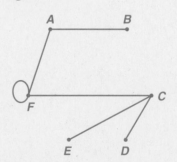

Glencoe Division, Macmillan/McGraw-Hill

## 16-2 | Practice Worksheet

### Walks and Paths

*Use the graph below to determine whether each walk is a circuit, cycle, path, trail, or walk. Use the most specific name.*

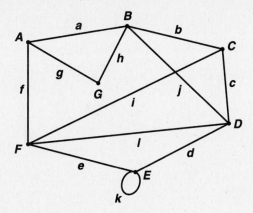

**1.** $a, h, g$

**2.** $a, b, c, j, a$

**3.** $i, c, d$

**4.** $e, d, c, i$

**5.** $k$

**6.** $f, g, h, a$

*For each multigraph below, list one of the paths from A to B and state its length.*

**7.**

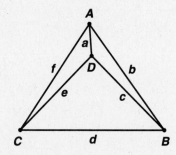

**8.**

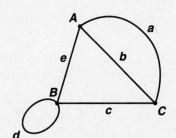

**9.**

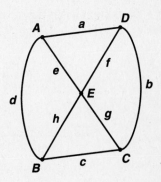

Glencoe Division, Macmillan/McGraw-Hill

16-2 **Practice Worksheet**

## Walks and Paths

*Use the graph below to determine whether each walk is a circuit, cycle, path, trail, or walk. Use the most specific name.*

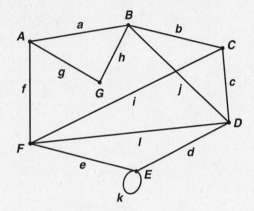

1. $a, h, g$  **cycle**

2. $a, b, c, j, a$  **walk**

3. $i, c, d$  **path**

4. $e, d, c, i$  **circuit**

5. $k$  **cycle**

6. $f, g, h, a$  **trail**

*For each multigraph below, list one of the paths from A to B and state its length.*

**Sample answers are given.**

7.

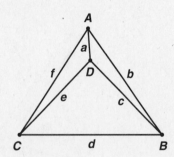

8.

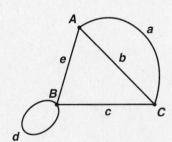

9.

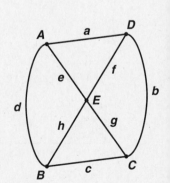

*a, c*; 2          *b, c*; 2          *a, f, h*; 3

Glencoe Division, Macmillan/McGraw-Hill

# Practice Worksheet

## Euler Paths and Circuits

*Determine whether each multigraph has an Euler path. Write yes or no.*

**1.**

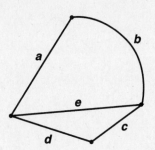

**2.**

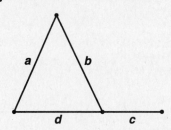

**3.**

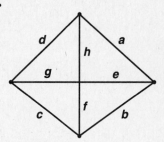

**4.**

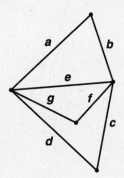

**5.**

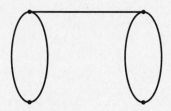

**6.**

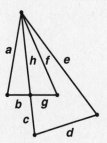

*Determine whether each multigraph has an Euler circuit. Write yes or no.*

**7.**

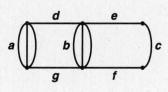

**8.**

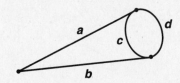

**9.**

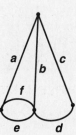

**10.**

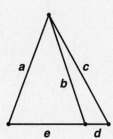

**11.**

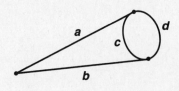

**12.**

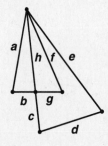

Glencoe Division, Macmillan/McGraw-Hill

# Practice Worksheet

## Euler Paths and Circuits

**Determine whether each multigraph has an Euler path. Write yes or no.**

**1.** yes

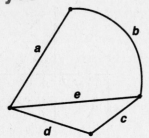

**2.** no

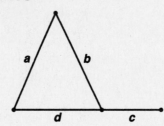

**3.** no

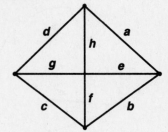

**4.** yes

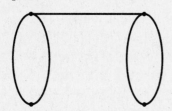

**5.** yes

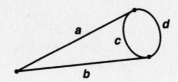

**6.** no

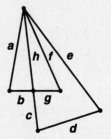

**Determine whether each multigraph has an Euler circuit. Write yes or no.**

**7.** yes

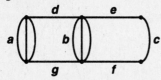

**8.** no

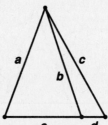

**9.** no

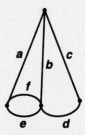

**10.** yes

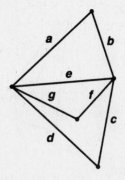

**11.** yes

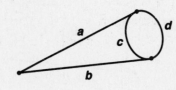

**12.** no

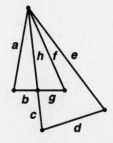

Glencoe Division, Macmillan/McGraw-Hill

16-4

# Practice Worksheet

## Shortest Paths and Minimal Distances

*Determine the distance and shortest path from A to Z in the graphs below by using the breadth-first search algorithm.*

**1.**

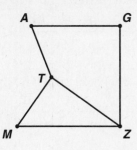

**2.**

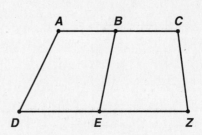

**3.**

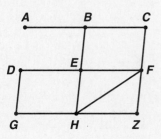

**4.**

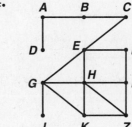

*Determine the distance from A to all of the other vertices. Then find a minimal path and the minimal distance from A to Z by using Dijkstra's algorithm.*

**5.**

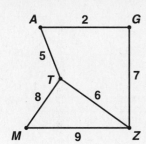

**6.**

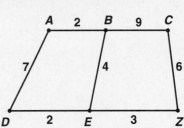

**7.**

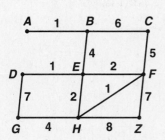

**8.**

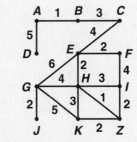

Glencoe Division, Macmillan/McGraw-Hill

16-4

# Practice Worksheet

## Shortest Paths and Minimal Distances

**Determine the distance and shortest path from A to Z in the graphs below by using the breadth-first search algorithm.**

**1.**

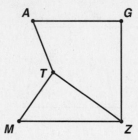

2; one path is *A, T, Z.*

**2.**

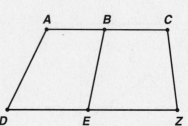

3; one path is *A, B, C, Z.*

**3.**

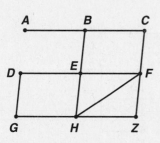

4; one path is *A, B, E, H, Z.*

**4.**

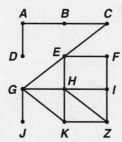

5; *A, B, C, E, H, Z*

**Determine the distance from A to all of the other vertices. Then find a minimal path and the minimal distance from A to Z by using Dijkstra's algorithm.**

**5.**

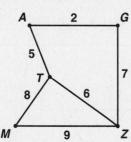

9; *A, G, Z*

**6.**

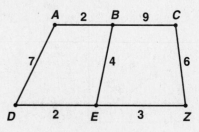

9; *A, B, E, Z*

**7.**

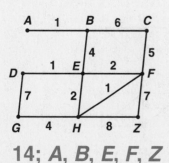

14; *A, B, E, F, Z*

**8.**

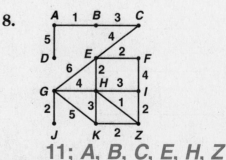

11; *A, B, C, E, H, Z*

Glencoe Division, Macmillan/McGraw-Hill

16-5 | # Practice Worksheet

## Trees

**Determine whether each graph is a tree. Write yes or no. If, no explain.**

1.

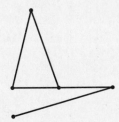

2.

3.

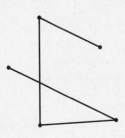

### Solve.

4. How many vertices are there in a tree with 25 edges?

5. How many edges are there in a tree with 20 vertices?

**Find a spanning tree for each graph.**

6.

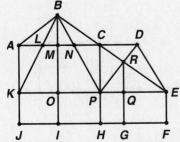

7.

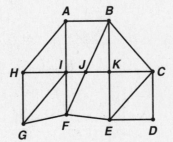

8.

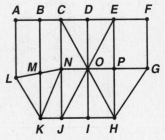

9.

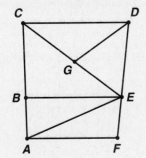

10.

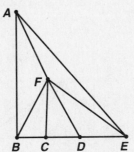

11.

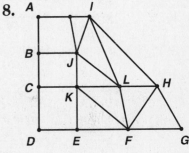

**Find a minimal spanning tree for each weighted graph. State the weight of the tree.**

12.

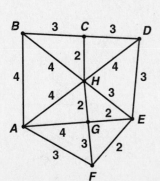

13.

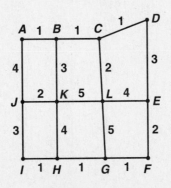

14.

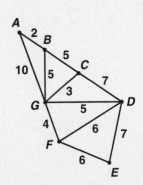

Glencoe Division, Macmillan/McGraw-Hill

# 16-5 Practice Worksheet

## Trees

**Determine whether each graph is a tree. Write yes or no. If, no explain.**

1.

2. yes

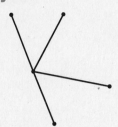

3. yes

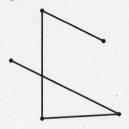

**No; there is more than one path between any two vertices.**

**Solve.**

4. How many vertices are there in a tree with 25 edges?
   26

5. How many edges are there in a tree with 20 vertices?
   19

**Find a spanning tree for each graph.** Answers may vary.

6.

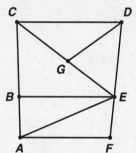

7.

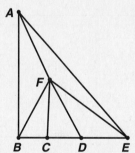

8.

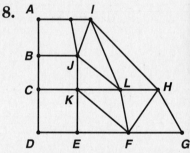

9.

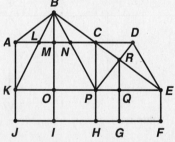

10.

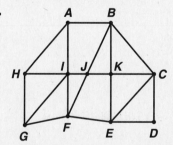

11.

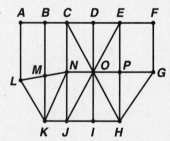

**Find a minimal spanning tree for each weighted graph. State the weight of the tree.**

12. 17

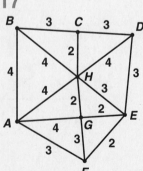

13. 18

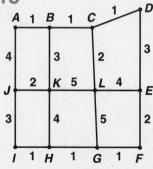

14. 25

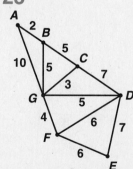

Glencoe Division, Macmillan/McGraw-Hill

NAME _____ DATE _____

# Practice Worksheet

## Graphs and Matrices

**Find M(G) for each graph.**

1.
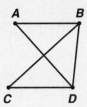

2.
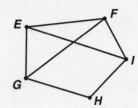

**Find M(G) for each digraph.**

3.
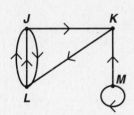

4.
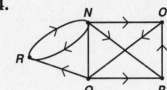

**Draw the graph for which each matrix is M(G).**

5.
$$\begin{array}{c}\phantom{A}\begin{array}{cc}A & B\end{array}\\ \begin{array}{c}A\\B\end{array}\left[\begin{array}{cc}0 & 1\\1 & 1\end{array}\right]\end{array}$$

6.
$$\begin{array}{c}\phantom{D}\begin{array}{ccc}D & E & F\end{array}\\ \begin{array}{c}D\\E\\F\end{array}\left[\begin{array}{ccc}0 & 1 & 2\\2 & 0 & 1\\1 & 1 & 0\end{array}\right]\end{array}$$

7.
$$\begin{array}{c}\phantom{G}\begin{array}{ccc}G & H & I\end{array}\\ \begin{array}{c}G\\H\\I\end{array}\left[\begin{array}{ccc}1 & 0 & 1\\1 & 0 & 0\\0 & 1 & 0\end{array}\right]\end{array}$$

8.
$$\begin{array}{c}\phantom{J}\begin{array}{cccc}J & K & L & M\end{array}\\ \begin{array}{c}J\\K\\L\\M\end{array}\left[\begin{array}{cccc}0 & 1 & 1 & 2\\1 & 0 & 1 & 1\\0 & 2 & 0 & 1\\1 & 1 & 1 & 1\end{array}\right]\end{array}$$

## 16-6  Practice Worksheet

## Graphs and Matrices

**Find M(G) for each graph.**

**1.**

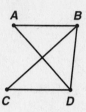

$$
\begin{array}{c}
\phantom{A}\begin{array}{cccc} A & B & C & D \end{array}\\
\begin{array}{c} A \\ B \\ C \\ D \end{array}
\left[\begin{array}{cccc}
0 & 1 & 0 & 1 \\
1 & 0 & 1 & 1 \\
0 & 1 & 0 & 1 \\
1 & 1 & 1 & 0
\end{array}\right]
\end{array}
$$

**2.**

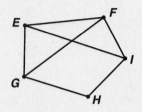

$$
\begin{array}{c}
\phantom{E}\begin{array}{ccccc} E & F & G & H & I \end{array}\\
\begin{array}{c} E \\ F \\ G \\ H \\ I \end{array}
\left[\begin{array}{ccccc}
0 & 1 & 1 & 0 & 1 \\
1 & 0 & 1 & 0 & 1 \\
1 & 1 & 0 & 1 & 0 \\
0 & 0 & 1 & 0 & 1 \\
1 & 1 & 0 & 1 & 0
\end{array}\right]
\end{array}
$$

**Find M(G) for each digraph.**

**3.**

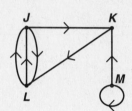

$$
\begin{array}{c}
\phantom{J}\begin{array}{cccc} J & K & L & M \end{array}\\
\begin{array}{c} J \\ K \\ L \\ M \end{array}
\left[\begin{array}{cccc}
0 & 1 & 1 & 0 \\
0 & 0 & 1 & 0 \\
2 & 0 & 0 & 0 \\
0 & 1 & 0 & 1
\end{array}\right]
\end{array}
$$

**4.**

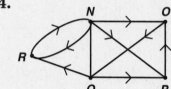

$$
\begin{array}{c}
\phantom{N}\begin{array}{ccccc} N & O & P & Q & R \end{array}\\
\begin{array}{c} N \\ O \\ P \\ Q \\ R \end{array}
\left[\begin{array}{ccccc}
0 & 1 & 1 & 0 & 1 \\
0 & 0 & 0 & 1 & 0 \\
0 & 1 & 0 & 0 & 0 \\
1 & 0 & 1 & 0 & 1 \\
1 & 0 & 0 & 0 & 0
\end{array}\right]
\end{array}
$$

**Draw the graph for which each matrix is M(G).**  Sample answers are given.

**5.**
$$
\begin{array}{c}
\phantom{A}\begin{array}{cc} A & B \end{array}\\
\begin{array}{c} A \\ B \end{array}
\left[\begin{array}{cc}
0 & 1 \\
1 & 1
\end{array}\right]
\end{array}
$$

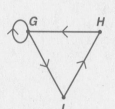

**6.**
$$
\begin{array}{c}
\phantom{D}\begin{array}{ccc} D & E & F \end{array}\\
\begin{array}{c} D \\ E \\ F \end{array}
\left[\begin{array}{ccc}
0 & 1 & 2 \\
2 & 0 & 1 \\
1 & 1 & 0
\end{array}\right]
\end{array}
$$

**7.**
$$
\begin{array}{c}
\phantom{G}\begin{array}{ccc} G & H & I \end{array}\\
\begin{array}{c} G \\ H \\ I \end{array}
\left[\begin{array}{ccc}
1 & 0 & 1 \\
1 & 0 & 0 \\
0 & 1 & 0
\end{array}\right]
\end{array}
$$

**8.**
$$
\begin{array}{c}
\phantom{J}\begin{array}{cccc} J & K & L & M \end{array}\\
\begin{array}{c} J \\ K \\ L \\ M \end{array}
\left[\begin{array}{cccc}
0 & 1 & 1 & 2 \\
1 & 0 & 1 & 1 \\
0 & 2 & 0 & 1 \\
1 & 1 & 1 & 1
\end{array}\right]
\end{array}
$$

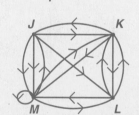

Glencoe Division, Macmillan/McGraw-Hill

## 17-1 **Practice Worksheet**

### *Limits*

**Evaluate each limit.**

**1.** $\lim\limits_{x \to 3} (x^2 + 3x - 8)$

**2.** $\lim\limits_{x \to 0} (2x + 7)$

**3.** $\lim\limits_{n \to 0} \left( 4n - \dfrac{1}{4n} \right)$

**4.** $\lim\limits_{n \to 0} \left( 3 \cdot 6n + 2 \cdot \dfrac{1}{6n} \right)$

**5.** $\lim\limits_{x \to 5} \dfrac{x^2 - 25}{x - 5}$

**6.** $\lim\limits_{x \to 2} \dfrac{x^2 - 5x + 6}{x - 2}$

**7.** $\lim\limits_{x \to 2} \dfrac{x - 2}{x^2 - 4}$

**8.** $\lim\limits_{x \to 3} \dfrac{x^2 - 9}{x^3 - 27}$

**9.** $\lim\limits_{x \to 2} \sqrt{2x^2 + 1}$

**10.** $\lim\limits_{x \to 4} \sqrt{x^2 - 2x + 1}$

**Evaluate the limit of f(g(x)) as x approaches 2 for each f(x) and g(x).**

**11.** $f(x) = 3x - 1$
$g(x) = 2x + 5$

**12.** $f(x) = 2x - 6$
$g(x) = 3x + 2$

**13.** $f(x) = x^2 + 1$
$g(x) = x + 7$

**14.** $f(x) = 3x + 1$
$g(x) = 2x^2 - 1$

Glencoe Division, Macmillan/McGraw-Hill

**17-1** **Practice Worksheet**

## Limits

**Evaluate each limit.**

1. $\lim\limits_{x \to 3} (x^2 + 3x - 8)$

   10

2. $\lim\limits_{x \to 0} (2x + 7)$

   7

3. $\lim\limits_{n \to 0} \left(4n - \dfrac{1}{4n}\right)$

   0

4. $\lim\limits_{n \to 0} \left(3 \cdot 6n + 2 \cdot \dfrac{1}{6n}\right)$

   5

5. $\lim\limits_{x \to 5} \dfrac{x^2 - 25}{x - 5}$

   10

6. $\lim\limits_{x \to 2} \dfrac{x^2 - 5x + 6}{x - 2}$

   $-1$

7. $\lim\limits_{x \to 2} \dfrac{x - 2}{x^2 - 4}$

   $\dfrac{1}{4}$

8. $\lim\limits_{x \to 3} \dfrac{x^2 - 9}{x^3 - 27}$

   $\dfrac{2}{9}$

9. $\lim\limits_{x \to 2} \sqrt{2x^2 + 1}$

   3

10. $\lim\limits_{x \to 4} \sqrt{x^2 - 2x + 1}$

    3

**Evaluate the limit of f(g(x)) as x approaches 2 for each f(x) and g(x).**

11. $f(x) = 3x - 1$
    $g(x) = 2x + 5$
    26

12. $f(x) = 2x - 6$
    $g(x) = 3x + 2$
    10

13. $f(x) = x^2 + 1$
    $g(x) = x + 7$
    82

14. $f(x) = 3x + 1$
    $g(x) = 2x^2 - 1$
    22

Glencoe Division, Macmillan/McGraw-Hill

# 17-2 Practice Worksheet

## Derivatives and Differentiation Techniques

*Find the derivative of each function.*

**1.** $f(x) = 2x^2 - 3x$

**2.** $f(x) = 6x^3 - 2x + 5$

**3.** $f(x) = 3x^7 + 4x^5 - 2x^2$

**4.** $f(x) = 3x^{15} - 12x^{10} + 7x^2 - 8$

**5.** $f(x) = (2x + 7)(3x - 8)$

**6.** $f(x) = (x^2 + 1)(3x - 2)$

**7.** $f(x) = (x^2 + 5x)^2$

**8.** $f(x) = (x^2 - 2x + 1)^3$

**9.** $f(x) = x^2(x^3 + 3x^2)$

**10.** $f(x) = (x^2 + 2x)(x^2 + 7x)$

**11.** $f(x) = x^2(x^4 + 2x)^2$

**12.** $f(x) = (x^2 + 3x)(x^2 + 2x)^2$

**13.** $f(x) = \dfrac{x^2}{x - 1}$

**14.** $f(x) = \dfrac{x^2 - 3x + 1}{2x - 9}$

**15.** $f(x) = \sqrt{2x^2 + 7x - 8}$

**16.** $f(x) = \sqrt[3]{x^2 + 1}$

Glencoe Division, Macmillan/McGraw-Hill

## 17-2 **Practice Worksheet**

## *Derivatives and Differentiation Techniques*

*Find the derivative of each function.*

**1.** $f(x) = 2x^2 - 3x$
$4x - 3$

**2.** $f(x) = 6x^3 - 2x + 5$
$18x^2 - 2$

**3.** $f(x) = 3x^7 + 4x^5 - 2x^2$
$-21x^6 + 20x^4 - 4x$

**4.** $f(x) = 3x^{15} - 12x^{10} + 7x^2 - 8$
$45x^{14} - 120x^9 + 14x$

**5.** $f(x) = (2x + 7)(3x - 8)$
$12x + 5$

**6.** $f(x) = (x^2 + 1)(3x - 2)$
$9x^2 - 4x + 3$

**7.** $f(x) = (x^2 + 5x)^2$
$4x^3 + 30x^2 + 50x$

**8.** $f(x) = (x^2 - 2x + 1)^3$
$6x^5 - 30x^4 + 60x^3 - 60x^2 + 30x - 6$

**9.** $f(x) = x^2(x^3 + 3x^2)$
$5x^4 + 12x^3$

**10.** $f(x) = (x^2 + 2x)(x^2 + 7x)$
$4x^3 + 27x^2 + 28x$

**11.** $f(x) = x^2(x^4 + 2x)^2$
$10x^9 + 28x^6 + 16x^3$

**12.** $f(x) = (x^2 + 3x)(x^2 + 2x)^2$
$6x^5 + 35x^4 + 64x^3 + 36x^2$

**13.** $f(x) = \dfrac{x^2}{x - 1}$

$\dfrac{x^2 - 2x}{(x - 1)^2}$

**14.** $f(x) = \dfrac{x^2 - 3x + 1}{2x - 9}$

$\dfrac{2x^2 - 18x + 25}{(2x - 9)^2}$

**15.** $f(x) = \sqrt{2x^2 + 7x - 8}$

$\dfrac{4x + 7}{2\sqrt{2x^2 + 7x - 8}}$

**16.** $f(x) = \sqrt[3]{x^2 + 1}$

$\dfrac{2x}{3\sqrt[3]{(x^2 + 1)^2}}$

Glencoe Division, Macmillan/McGraw-Hill

## 17-3 **Practice Worksheet**

### *Area Under a Curve*

**Write a limit to find the area between each curve and the x-axis for the given interval. Then find the area.**

**1.** $y = x^2$ from $x = 1$ to $x = 6$

**2.** $y = x^3$ from $x = 1$ to $x = 5$

**3.** $y = x^4$ from $x = 1$ to $x = 3$

**4.** $y = x^5$ from $x = 2$ to $x = 5$

## 17-3 Practice Worksheet

### Area Under a Curve

**Write a limit to find the area between each curve and the x-axis for the given interval. Then find the area.**

**1.** $y = x^2$ from $x = 1$ to $x = 6$

$$A = \lim_{n \to \infty} \sum_{i=1}^{n} \left(\frac{6i}{n}\right)^2 \left(\frac{6}{n}\right) -$$

$$\lim_{n \to \infty} \sum_{i=1}^{n} \left(\frac{i}{n}\right)^2 \left(\frac{1}{n)}\right);$$

$71\frac{2}{3}$ square units

**2.** $y = x^3$ from $x = 1$ to $x = 5$

$$A = \lim_{n \to \infty} \sum_{i=1}^{n} \left(\frac{5i}{n}\right)^3 \left(\frac{5}{n}\right) -$$

$$\lim_{n \to \infty} \sum_{i=1}^{n} \left(\frac{i}{n}\right)^3 \left(\frac{1}{n}\right);$$

156 square units

**3.** $y = x^4$ from $x = 1$ to $x = 3$

$$A = \lim_{n \to \infty} \sum_{i=1}^{n} \left(\frac{3i}{n}\right)^4 \left(\frac{3}{n}\right) -$$

$$\lim_{n \to \infty} \sum_{i=1}^{n} \left(\frac{i}{n}\right)^4 \left(\frac{1}{n}\right);$$

$48\frac{2}{5}$ square units

**4.** $y = x^5$ from $x = 2$ to $x = 5$

$$A = \lim_{n \to \infty} \sum_{i=1}^{n} \left(\frac{5i}{n}\right)^3 \left(\frac{5}{n}\right) -$$

$$\lim_{n \to \infty} \sum_{i=1}^{n} \left(\frac{2i}{n}\right)^5 \left(\frac{2}{n}\right);$$

$2593\frac{1}{2}$ square units

Glencoe Division, Macmillan/McGraw-Hill

# 17-4 Practice Worksheet

## *Integration*

**Find each integral.**

**1.** $\int 8\, dx$

**2.** $\int (2x + 6)\, dx$

**3.** $\int (6x^2 - 12x + 8)\, dx$

**4.** $\int (9x^2 + 12x - 9)\, dx$

**5.** $\int (x - 2)^{10}\, dx$

**6.** $\int 2(2x - 3)^4\, dx$

**7.** $\int (5 - x)^6\, dx$

**8.** $\int (3x - 1)^4\, dx$

**9.** $\int \frac{1}{x + 2}\, dx$

**10.** $\int \frac{3}{x - 4}\, dx$

**11.** $\int 3x^2 \sqrt{x^3 + 5}\, dx$

**12.** $\int x \sqrt[3]{x^2 - 5}\, dx$

**13.** $\int \frac{10}{x^2}\, dx$

**14.** $\int \frac{4}{x^3}\, dx$

Glencoe Division, Macmillan/McGraw-Hill

# 17-4 Practice Worksheet

## Integration

**Find each integral.**

1. $\int 8\,dx$

$$8x + C$$

2. $\int (2x + 6)\,dx$

$$x^2 + 6x + C$$

3. $\int (6x^2 - 12x + 8)\,dx$

$$2x^3 - 6x^2 + 8x + C$$

4. $\int (9x^2 + 12x - 9)\,dx$

$$3x^3 + 6x^2 - 9x + C$$

5. $\int (x - 2)^{10}\,dx$

$$\frac{(x - 2)^{11}}{11} + C$$

6. $\int 2(2x - 3)^4\,dx$

$$\frac{(2x - 3)^5}{5} + C$$

7. $\int (5 - x)^6\,dx$

$$-\frac{(5 - x)^7}{7} + C$$

8. $\int (3x - 1)^4\,dx$

$$\frac{(3x - 1)^5}{15} + C$$

9. $\int \frac{1}{x + 2}\,dx$

$$\ln |x + 2| + C$$

10. $\int \frac{3}{x - 4}\,dx$

$$3 \ln |x - 4| + C$$

11. $\int 3x^2 \sqrt{x^3 + 5}\,dx$

$$\frac{2}{3} \sqrt{(x^3 + 5)^3} + C$$

12. $\int x \sqrt[3]{x^2 - 5}\,dx$

$$\frac{3}{8} \sqrt[3]{(x^2 - 5)^4} + C$$

13. $\int \frac{10}{x^2}\,dx$

$$-\frac{10}{x} + C$$

14. $\int \frac{4}{x^3}\,dx$

$$-\frac{2}{x^2} + C$$

Glencoe Division, Macmillan/McGraw-Hill

## 17-5 Practice Worksheet

## The Fundamental Theorem of Calculus

*Use integration to find the area of each shaded region.*

1.

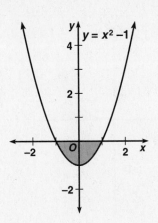

2.

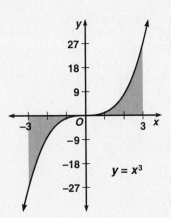

*Evaluate each definite integral.*

3. $\displaystyle\int_2^5 2x\, dx$

4. $\displaystyle\int_{-2}^1 (x+1)^3\, dx$

5. $\displaystyle\int_2^6 (4x^3 - 3x^2)\, dx$

6. $\displaystyle\int_{-1}^4 (2x^3 - 6x^2 + 7)\, dx$

7. $\displaystyle\int_{-2}^1 (x-1)(x+3)\, dx$

8. $\displaystyle\int_{-3}^2 (2x+1)(2x-1)\, dx$

9. $\displaystyle\int_0^2 2x(x^2+2)^2\, dx$

10. $\displaystyle\int_{-1}^1 (3x^2+2x)(x^3+x^2)^2\, dx$

Glencoe Division, Macmillan/McGraw-Hill

**17-5** **Practice Worksheet**

## The Fundamental Theorem of Calculus

*Use integration to find the area of each shaded region.*

**1.**

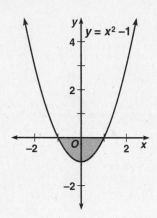

$1\dfrac{1}{3}$ sq. units

**2.**

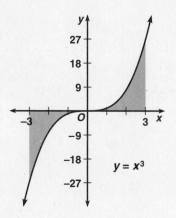

$40\dfrac{1}{2}$ sq. units

**Evaluate each definite integral.**

**3.** $\displaystyle\int_{2}^{5} 2x \, dx$

**21**

**4.** $\displaystyle\int_{-2}^{1} (x + 1)^3 \, dx$

$3\dfrac{3}{4}$

**5.** $\displaystyle\int_{2}^{6} (4x^3 - 3x^2) \, dx$

**1072**

**6.** $\displaystyle\int_{-1}^{4} (2x^3 - 6x^2 + 7) \, dx$

$32\dfrac{1}{2}$

**7.** $\displaystyle\int_{-2}^{1} (x - 1)(x + 3) \, dx$

**−9**

**8.** $\displaystyle\int_{-3}^{2} (2x + 1)(2x - 1) \, dx$

$41\dfrac{2}{3}$

**9.** $\displaystyle\int_{0}^{2} 2x(x^2 + 2)^2 \, dx$

$69\dfrac{1}{3}$

**10.** $\displaystyle\int_{-1}^{1} (3x^2 + 2x)(x^3 + x^2)^2 \, dx$

$2\dfrac{2}{3}$

Glencoe Division, Macmillan/McGraw-Hill